McDOUGAL LITTELL
— The —
AMERICANS
Reconstruction to the 21st Century

CURRICULUM

In-Depth Resources: Unit 3

Modern America Emerges

McDougal Littell
A HOUGHTON MIFFLIN COMPANY
Evanston, Illinois • Boston • Dallas

Acknowledgments

CHAPTER 10

Excerpt from *Hawaii* by James A. Michener. Copyright © 1959 by James A. Michener. Reprinted by permission of Random House, Inc.

CHAPTER 11

Lyrics to "Over There" by George M. Cohen. Reprinted by permission of EMI Music Publishing Inc.

Excerpt from *A Son at the Front* by Edith Wharton. Copyright 1923 by Edith Wharton, renewed 1951 by William F. Tyler. Reprinted by permission of the Estate of Edith Wharton and the Watkins/Loomis Agency.

Excerpt from "In Another Country," from *Men Without Women* by Ernest Hemingway. Copyright 1927 by Charles Scribner's Sons. Copyright renewed 1955 by Ernest Hemingway. Reprinted with the permission of Scribner, a division of Simon & Schuster.

ISBN-13: 978-0-618-17608-3   ISBN-10: 0-618-17608-X

Printed in the United States of America.

10 11 12 – MDO – 08 07 06

CHAPTER ⓫ The First World War, 1914–1920

Name _____ Date _____

GUIDED READING *The Origins of Progressivism*

A. As you read about the era of reform, take notes about the goals, reformers, and successes of the reform movements.

Social Reforms	People and Groups Involved	Successes (laws, legal decisions, etc.)
1. Social welfare reform movement		
2. Moral reform movement		
3. Economic reform movement		
4. Movement for industrial efficiency		
5. Movement to protect workers		

Political Reforms	People and Groups Involved	Successes (laws, legal decisions, etc.)
6. Movement to reform local government		
7. State reform of big business		
8. Movement for election reform		

B. On the back of this paper, explain the importance of the following:

    progressive movement   **prohibition**   **scientific management**

Name _____ Date _____

CHAPTER **9** Section 2

GUIDED READING *Women in Public Life*

A. As you read this section, take notes to answer the questions.

1. What types of jobs were women in each group likely to hold?			
Lower Class	Middle and Upper Class	African American	Immigrant

2. How did educational opportunities for middle- and upper-class women change?
3. How did these new opportunities affect the lives of middle- and upper-class women?

4. What three strategies were adopted by the suffragists to win the vote?		
a.	b.	c.

5. What results did each strategy produce?		
a.	b.	c.

B. On the back of this paper, explain the significance of each of the following:

NACW   Susan B. Anthony   NAWSA

Name _____ Date _____

CHAPTER 9

Section 3

GUIDED READING *Teddy Roosevelt's Square Deal*

A. As you read this section, write notes to answer questions about President Theodore Roosevelt. If Roosevelt took no steps to solve the problem or if no legislation was involved in solving the problem, write "none."

Problem	What steps did Roosevelt take to solve each problem?	Which legislation helped solve the problem?
1. 1902 coal strike		
2. Trusts		
3. Unregulated big business		
4. Dangerous foods and medicines		
5. Shrinking wilderness and natural resources		
6. Racial discrimination		

B. On the back of this paper, explain the importance of each of the following:

Square Deal   *The Jungle*   **Upton Sinclair**   **NAACP**

Name _____ Date _____

GUIDED READING *Progressivism Under Taft*

A. As you read this section, take notes to answer questions about growing conflicts between reform and business interests.

In 1912, the Republican Party splits at its convention.

	Progressives	Conservatives
1. Why did they support or oppose Taft?		
2. What party did they form or stay with?		

In the 1912 election, four parties run candidates.

	Progressive Party	Republican Party	Democratic Party	Socialist Party
3. Who did they run for president?				
4. What was their candidate's position on big business?				

B. On the back of this paper, explain why **Gifford Pinchot** is an important figure in U.S. history.

Name _____ Date _____

As you read about President Wilson's approach to reform, take notes
to answer the questions.

What were the aims of each piece of legislation or constitutional amendment?	
1. Federal Trade Act	
2. Clayton Antitrust Act	
3. Underwood Tariff	
4. Sixteenth Amendment	
5. Federal Reserve Act	

6. Which three new developments finally brought the success of the woman suffrage movement within reach?
7. Which constitutional amendment recognized women's right to vote?

8. How did Wilson retreat on civil rights?

CHAPTER 9

BUILDING VOCABULARY *The Progressive Era*

A. Matching Match the description in the second column with the term or name in the first column. Write the appropriate letter next to the word.

_____ 1. suffrage   a. name of Roosevelt's reform measures

_____ 2. Woodrow Wilson   b. journalists who uncovered corruption

_____ 3. Nineteenth Amendment   c. the right to vote

_____ 4. muckrakers   d. progressive party headed by Roosevelt

_____ 5. conservation   e. granted suffrage for women

_____ 6. Prohibition   f. sought to curb growth of monopolies

_____ 7. Florence Kelley   g. advocate for women and children

_____ 8. Clayton Antitrust Act   h. winner of 1912 presidential election

_____ 9. Bull-Moose Party   i. the banning of alcoholic beverages

_____ 10. Square Deal   j. preservation of natural resources

B. Evaluating Write *T* in the blank if the statement is true. If the statement is false, write *F* in the blank and then write the corrected statement on the line below.

_____ 1. Susan B. Anthony was a leading proponent of woman suffrage.

_____

_____ 2. The major goal of the prominent progressive governor Robert M. La Follette was reforming the nation's education system.

_____

_____ 3. The goal of the NAACP was full voting rights for women.

_____

_____ 4. Upton Sinclair was the author of *The Jungle*, a critical look at the nation's meatpacking industry.

_____

_____ 5. The progressive movement aimed at returning control of government to the people, restoring economic opportunities, and correcting injustices in American life.

_____

C. Writing Write a paragraph describing some of the significant political reforms during the Progressive Era using the following terms.

initiative   **referendum**   **recall**   **Seventeenth Amendment**

CHAPTER **9** Section 1

SKILLBUILDER PRACTICE *Forming Historical Questions*

In the years following the turn of the century, many women and children could find no other means of survival than to work long hours in unsafe conditions. Progressive reformers sought to end unfair treatment by employers. Read the passage below by a progressive reformer about child labor in Pennsylvania's anthracite coal-mining region. Think of questions that would lead you to find out more about the situation. Fill in the chart with a question for each category. (See Skillbuilder Handbook, p. R12.)

The slate is sharp so that the slate pickers often cut or bruise their hands; the coal is carried down the chute in water and this means sore and swollen hands for the pickers. The first few weeks after a boy begins work, his fingers bleed almost continuously and are called red tops by the other boys. Slate picking is not itself dangerous; the slate picker is, however, sometimes set at cleaning-up jobs, which require him to clean out shakers, the chute, or other machinery. . . .

Accidents that had occurred to boys in the breakers as well as underground were recounted to the Children's Bureau agents. One boy told of a friend who had dropped a new cap in the rollers and how, in trying to pull it out, his arm was caught, crushed, and twisted. The older brother of another boy, a jig runner, slipped while at work and his arm was caught in the jig [a sorting machine] and mashed. One boy told of the death of another while watching the dam beneath the breaker. He and some of the other breaker boys had helped to extricate the mutilated body from the wheels in which their companion was caught; he himself had held the bag into which the recovered parts of the dead body were put.

As reported by the boys, 42 percent of these accidents kept them from work less than two weeks. . . . According to the reports made to the Children's Bureau, no compensation was paid forty-four boys who were incapacitated for a period of two weeks or more as the result of injuries received while they were employed in the mines, although the Pennsylvania Compensation Law entitled them to receive it.

It would be superfluous to point out that in view of the hazards of mining, young boys should not be employed in the mines or around the breakers. Public opinion had already prohibited underground work in Pennsylvania and in most other states, and the federal government had imposed a penalty in the form of a tax if children under sixteen were employed in or about a mine. The real problem here, as in many other parts of the country, was how to secure the enforcement of the child labor laws that had been enacted.

from U. S. Department of Labor, *Child Labor and the Welfare of Children in an Anthracite Coal-Mining District* (Washington, D. C.: Children's Bureau Publication No. 106, 1922).

Your Questions
Who?
What?
When?
Where?
Why?
How?

Name _____ Date _____

Analyzing

Complete the chart below by identifying the four goals of progressivism and providing examples of how reformers tried to meet each goal.

Goals of Progressivism

Goal:	Goal:	Goal:	Goal:

Examples:	Examples:	Examples:	Examples:

CHAPTER 9 Section 2

RETEACHING ACTIVITY *Women in Public Life*

Finding Main Ideas

The following questions deal with reforms in public education. Answer them in the space provided.

1. What percentage of women held jobs by the turn of the 20th century? What types of work did they do?

   _____

   _____

2. How did many African-American women earn a living during the late 1800s?

   _____

   _____

3. Why were many women opposed to the Fourteenth and Fifteenth Amendments?

   _____

   _____

4. What were the main reform movements in which many women participated?

   _____

   _____

5. What groups opposed woman suffrage and why?

   _____

   _____

6. What were the three approaches suffragists tried to achieve their objectives?

   _____

   _____

CHAPTER 9
Section 3

RETEACHING ACTIVITY *Teddy Roosevelt's Square Deal*

Choose the best answer for each item. Write the letter of your answer in the blank.

_____ 1. Theodore Roosevelt's professional background included all of the following jobs except
    a. New York City police commissioner.
    b. U.S. senator.
    c. assistant secretary of the U.S. Navy.
    d. vice-president.

_____ 2. Roosevelt began a presidential precedent by intervening in a 1902 strike by the
    a. coal industry.
    b. oil industry.
    c. railroad industry.
    d. textile industry.

_____ 3. The measure that required truth in labeling on numerous products was the
    a. Hepburn Act.
    b. Meat Inspection Act.
    c. National Reclamation Act.
    d. Pure Food and Drug Act.

_____ 4. Roosevelt was criticized by some for not doing enough to champion
    a. conservation.
    b. trust busting.
    c. civil rights.
    d. railroad regulation.

_____ 5. Roosevelt led the effort to reform the meatpacking industry after reading
    a. *The Jungle*.
    b. *Uncle Tom's Cabin*.
    c. *The Shame of the Cities*.
    d. "The History of the Standard Oil Company."

_____ 6. Roosevelt was persuaded to set aside millions of acres of forest reserves by the naturalist and writer
    a. Gifford Pinchot.
    b. John Muir.
    c. Booker T. Washington.
    d. Upton Sinclair.

CHAPTER 9

Section 4

RETEACHING ACTIVITY *Progressivism Under Taft*

Evaluating

A. Write *T* in the blank if the statement is true. If the statement is false, write *F* in the blank and then write the corrected statement on the line below.

_____ 1. President Taft's secretary of the interior, Richard A. Ballinger, disapproved of conservationist controls of western lands.

_____

_____ 2. The presidential election of 1908 saw the emergence of new third party, the Progressive Party, also known as the Bull Moose Party.

_____

_____ 3. Woodrow Wilson, the 1912 Democratic presidential candidate, was a reform senator from New York.

_____

_____ 4. Progressives disapproved of the Payne-Aldrich Tariff.

_____

_____ 5. The Bull Moose Party finished a distant third to the Democrats and Republicans in the election of 1912.

Summarizing

B. Complete the chart below by listing the ways in which President Taft upset progressive reformers.

Taft Upset Progressives
1.
2.
3.

Name _____ Date _____

CHAPTER 9

Section 5

RETEACHING ACTIVITY *Wilson's New Freedom*

Reading Comprehension

Complete each sentence with the appropriate term or name.

Idaho	holding companies	labor unions
supported	Underwood Act	Nineteenth Amendment
segregationists	Square Deal	Princeton University
farm organizations	opposed	World War I
New Freedom	Kansas	monopolies

1. Before entering politics, Woodrow Wilson served as president of _____.

2. _____ was the name of Wilson's progressive programs.

3. The ultimate goal of the Clayton Antitrust Act was stopping the creation of _____.

4. Under the Clayton Act, _____ and _____ no longer would be subject to antitrust laws.

5. Wilson worked to ensure passage of the _____, which would substantially reduce tariff rates for the first time since the Civil War.

6. By 1910, women had voting rights in Wyoming, Utah, Colorado, Washington, and _____.

7. All women won the right to vote with passage of the _____.

8. Wilson upset civil rights proponents by placing _____ in charge of some federal agencies.

9. As president, Woodrow Wilson _____ federal antilynching legislation.

10. As _____ came to dominate Wilson's second term in office, the Progressive Era came to an end.

CHAPTER 9

Section 5

GEOGRAPHY APPLICATION: REGION

The Movement Toward Woman Suffrage

Directions: Read the paragraphs below and study the map carefully. Then answer the questions that follow.

In the late 1800s, new amendments to the U.S. Constitution that guaranteed voting rights still continued to exclude women. Therefore, suffragists concentrated on the regional level—seeking the passage of state constitutional amendments insuring women the right to vote. It was felt that this strategy could eventually force a federal amendment, and in a six-year period, four states granted women full voting rights.

However, the campaign then stalled. For 13 years, until 1910, no other state passed an amendment for woman suffrage. So a new tactic was tried: gaining partial voting rights. The U.S. Constitution allows state legislatures to set qualifications for voting for presidential electors, without sending the question to voters as an attempt for an amendment requires. Thus, women pressed states for the right to vote for president through legislative action.

In Illinois, where Progressives controlled the state legislature, the plan worked. This state, in 1913, became the first to grant women partial suffrage. Grace Wilbur Trout wrote of its impact:

Illinois was the first state east of the Mississippi and the first state even bordering the great father of waters, to break down the conservatism of the great Middle West and give suffrage to its women. . . . New York women never could have won their great suffrage victory in 1917 if Illinois had not first opened the door in 1913, and the winning of suffrage in New York so added to the political strength of the suffrage movement in Congress that it made possible the passage of the federal suffrage amendment in 1919.

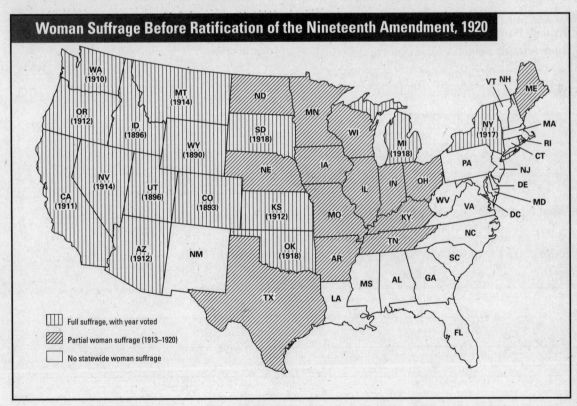

Woman Suffrage Before Ratification of the Nineteenth Amendment, 1920

WA (1910)
MT (1914)
ND
VT NH
ME
OR (1912)
ID (1896)
SD (1918)
MN
WI
NY (1917)
MA
RI
MI (1918)
CT
WY (1890)
NE
IA
PA
NJ
NV (1914)
IL IN OH
DE
CA (1911)
UT (1896)
CO (1893)
KS (1912)
MO
WV VA
MD
DC
KY
NC
AZ (1912)
NM
OK (1918)
AR
TN
SC
TX
LA
MS AL GA
FL

Full suffrage, with year voted
Partial woman suffrage (1913–1920)
No statewide woman suffrage

Interpreting Text and Visuals

1. Which was the first state to grant full suffrage to women? _____

   How many years before ratification of the Nineteenth Amendment did
   this happen? _____

2. Which other states granted full suffrage to women in the 19th century? _____
   _____

3. Where, in general, were the states that granted women full suffrage
   before 1913 located? _____

   Where, in general, were the states located that failed to give women any voting rights
   before the ratification of the Nineteenth Amendment?
   _____

4. What was the importance of the year 1913 to the woman suffrage movement? _____
   _____
   _____

5. Explain how the indirect system of voting for president through electors
   inadvertently helped women gain partial suffrage in several states.
   _____
   _____
   _____
   _____

6. What type of suffrage did women gain in New York in 1917? _____

7. Summarize the movement toward woman suffrage from 1913 to 1920. _____
   _____
   _____
   _____
   _____
   _____

Name _____   Date _____

CHAPTER
9
Section 1

PRIMARY SOURCE Declaration of the WCTU

The Woman's Christian Temperance Union (WCTU) was founded in 1873 to promote the goal of prohibition. In 1902 the WCTU drew up the following declaration. What principles did members of the WCTU support?

We believe in the coming of His kingdom whose service is perfect freedom, because His laws, written in our members as well as in nature and in grace, are perfect, converting the soul.

We believe in the gospel of the Golden Rule, and that each man's habits of life should be an example safe and beneficent for every other man to follow.

We believe that God created both man and woman in His own image, and, therefore, we believe in one standard of purity for both men and women, and in the equal right of all to hold opinions and to express the same with equal freedom.

We believe in a living wage; in an eight-hour day; in courts of conciliation and arbitration; in justice as opposed to greed of gain; in "peace on earth and goodwill to men."

We therefore formulate and, for ourselves, adopt the following pledge, asking our sisters and brothers of a common danger and a common hope to make common cause with us in working its reasonable and helpful precepts into the practice of everyday life:

I hereby solemnly promise, *God helping me,* to abstain from all distilled, fermented, and malt liquors, including wine, beer, and cider, and to employ all proper means to discourage the use of and traffic in the same.

To conform and enforce the rationale of this pledge, we declare our purpose to educate the young; to form a better public sentiment; to reform so far as possible, by religious, ethical, and scientific means, the drinking classes; to seek the transforming power of Divine Grace for ourselves and all for whom we work, that they and we may willfully transcend no law of pure and wholesome living; and finally we pledge ourselves to labor and to pray that all of these principles, founded upon the Gospel of Christ, may be worked out into the customs of society and the laws of the land.

from National Woman's Christian Temperance Union, *Annual Leaflet,* 1902. Reprinted in Encyclopaedia Britannica, *1895–1904: Populism, Imperialism, and Reform,* vol.12 in *The Annals of America* (Chicago: Encyclopaedia Britannica, 1968), 503.

Discussion Questions

1. What were the WCTU's beliefs and principles?
2. What pledge did members of the WCTU take?
3. Progressive movements in the early 1900s had at least one of these goals: protecting social welfare, promoting moral improvement, creating economic reform, and fostering efficiency. According to their declaration, which goal or goals did members of the WCTU have?

CHAPTER 9

Section 1

PRIMARY SOURCE Child Labor in the Coal Mines

In 1919 the Children's Bureau of the U.S. Department of Labor studied child labor in Pennsylvania's anthracite coal-mining region. As you read this excerpt from the study, think about why progressive reformers sought to end child labor.

These breakers which tower above the town of Shenandoah to the east and the south and the west are great barnlike structures filled with chutes, sliding belts, and great crushing and sorting machines. Around these machines a scaffolding was built on which the workers stand or sit. The coal is raised from the mine to the top of the breaker and dumped down the chute into a crushing machine, which breaks it into somewhat smaller lumps. These are carried along a moving belt or gravity incline on each side of which men and boys stand or sit picking out pieces of slate and any coal which has slate mixed with it. The latter is carried into another crusher, where it is broken again and then carried down chutes to be sorted further by slate pickers or by sorting machines. After the coal has been broken and cleaned of slate or other alien materials, it is sorted by being shaken through a series of screens.

The work in the breakers might be described as disagreeable but much less hazardous than underground mining. As it is not heavy and does not require skill, young boys or the older men are employed. "If you don't die, you wind up in the breakers," one man said. Another remarked, "You begin at the breaker and you end at the breaker, broken yourself." These older men and boys worked in the constant roar which the coal makes as it rushes down the chute, is broken in the crushing machines, or sorted in the shakers. Black coal dust is everywhere, covering the windows and filling the air and the lungs of the workers.

The slate is sharp so that the slate pickers often cut or bruise their hands; the coal is carried down the chute in water and this means sore and swollen hands for the pickers. The first few weeks after a boy begins work, his fingers bleed almost continuously and are called red tops by the other boys. Slate picking is not itself dangerous; the slate picker is, however, sometimes set at cleaning-up jobs, which require him to clean out shakers, the chute, or other machinery. . . .

Accidents that had occurred to boys in the breakers as well as underground were recounted to the Children's Bureau agents. One boy told of a friend who had dropped a new cap in the rollers and how, in trying to pull it out, his arm was caught, crushed, and twisted. The older brother of another boy, a jig runner, slipped while at work and his arm was caught in the jig [a sorting machine] and mashed. One boy told of the death of another while watching the dam beneath the breaker. He and some of the other breaker boys had helped to extricate the mutilated body from the wheels in which their companion was caught; he himself had held the bag into which the recovered parts of the dead body were put.

As reported by the boys, 42 percent of these accidents kept them from work less than two weeks. . . . According to the reports made to the Children's Bureau, no compensation was paid forty-four boys who were incapacitated for a period of two weeks or more as the result of injuries received while they were employed in the mines, although the Pennsylvania Compensation Law entitled them to receive it.

It would be superfluous to point out that in view of the hazards of mining, young boys should not be employed in the mines or around the breakers. Public opinion had already prohibited underground work in Pennsylvania and in most other states, and the federal government had imposed a penalty in the form of a tax if children under sixteen were employed in or about a mine. The real problem here, as in many other parts of the country, was how to secure the enforcement of the child labor laws that had been enacted.

from U. S. Department of Labor, *Child Labor and the Welfare of Children in an Anthracite Coal-Mining District* (Washington, D. C.: Children's Bureau Publication No. 106, 1922).

Activity Options

1. Imagine you are a boy who works in the anthracite coal mines. Write a diary entry in which you describe your work life and then share it with classmates.
2. As a progressive reformer in the 1900s, write a letter to a newspaper editor. State your opinion on child labor in the coal mines based on your reading of this excerpt. Then read your letter to classmates.

Name _____   Date _____

PRIMARY SOURCE Political Poster

This political poster was prepared by the Massachusetts Woman Suffrage Association. What does the poster urge voters to support on November 2 and why?

Smithsonian Institution. Photo courtesy, Picture Research Consultants.

Research Options

1. Find out more about the methods that woman suffragists used to draw attention to their cause. Then discuss with your classmates which methods might still be used effectively today to convey a political message.

2. Research the National Association Opposed to Woman Suffrage formed in 1911. Who was its leader? Why did this organization oppose woman suffrage? To share your findings with the class, create an anti-suffrage poster that reflects this organization's position.

PRIMARY SOURCE *from* "The Status of Woman"
by Susan B. Anthony

For more than 50 years, Susan B. Anthony worked for woman suffrage. As you read this excerpt from an article Anthony wrote in 1897, think about her assessment of women's status before and after the Seneca Falls Woman's Rights Convention.

Fifty years ago woman in the United States was without a recognized individuality in any department of life. No provision was made in public or private schools for her education in anything beyond the rudimentary branches. An educated woman was a rarity and was gazed upon with something akin to awe. The women who were known in the world of letters, in the entire country, could be easily counted upon the ten fingers. . . .

Such was the helpless, dependent, fettered condition of woman when the first Woman's Rights Convention was called just forty-nine years ago, at Seneca Falls, N. Y., by Elizabeth Cady Stanton and Lucretia Mott. . . .

From that little convention at Seneca Falls, with a following of a handful of women scattered through half-a-dozen different states, we have now the great National Association, with headquarters in New York City, and auxiliaries in almost every state in the Union. These state bodies are effecting a thorough system of county and local organizations for the purpose of securing legislation favorable to women, and especially to obtain amendments to their state constitutions. As evidence of the progress of public opinion, more than half of the legislatures in session during the past winter have discussed and voted upon bills for the enfranchisement of women, and in most of them they were adopted by one branch and lost by a very small majority in the other. The legislatures of Washington and South Dakota have submitted woman-suffrage amendments to their electors for 1898, and vigorous campaigns will be made in those states during the next two years.

For a quarter of a century Wyoming has stood as a conspicuous object lesson in woman suffrage, and is now reinforced by the three neighboring states of Colorado, Utah, and Idaho. With this central group, standing on the very crest of the Rocky Mountains, the spirit of justice and freedom for women cannot fail to descend upon all the Western and Northwestern states. No one who makes a careful study of this question can help but believe that, in a very few years, all the states west of the Mississippi River will have enfranchised their women.

While the efforts of each state are concentrated upon its own legislature, all of the states combined in the national organization are directing their energies toward securing a Sixteenth Amendment to the Constitution of the United States. The demands of this body have been received with respectful and encouraging attention from Congress. . . .

Until woman has obtained "that right protective of all other rights—the ballot," this agitation must still go on, absorbing the time and energy of our best and strongest women. Who can measure the advantages that would result if the magnificent abilities of these women could be devoted to the needs of government, society, home, instead of being consumed in the struggle to obtain their birthright of individual freedom? Until this be gained we can never know, we cannot even prophesy, the capacity and power of woman for the uplifting of humanity.

It may be delayed longer than we think; it may be here sooner than we expect; but the day will come when man will recognize woman as his peer, not only at the fireside but in the councils of the nation. Then, and not until then, will there be the perfect comradeship, the ideal union between the sexes that shall result in the highest development of the race. What this shall be we may not attempt to define, but this we know, that only good can come to the individual or to the nation through the rendering of exact justice.

from Susan B. Anthony, "The Status of Woman, Past, Present, and Future," *Arena*, May 1897.

Discussion Questions

1. How does Anthony view the condition of women 50 years after the first Woman's Rights Convention was held?
2. How would you describe Anthony's attitude toward women gaining the right to vote?

CHAPTER **9**

Section 3

LITERATURE SELECTION *from The Jungle*
by Upton Sinclair

Upton Sinclair's shocking portrayal of Chicago slaughterhouses in the early 1900s, as seen through the eyes of Lithuanian immigrants, raised the public's awareness and prompted Congress to pass the Meat Inspection Act and the Pure Food and Drug Act. How do characters in this excerpt from his novel respond to working in a meatpacking plant?

Entering one of the Durham buildings, they [Jurgis and Jokubas] found a number of other visitors waiting; and before long there came a guide, to escort them through the place. They make a great feature of showing strangers through the packing plants, for it is a good advertisement. But *ponas* Jokubas whispered maliciously that the visitors did not see any more than the packers wanted them to.

They climbed a long series of stairways outside of the building, to the top of its five or six stories. Here was the chute, with its river of hogs, all patiently toiling upward; there was a place for them to rest to cool off, and then through another passageway they went into a room from which there is no returning for hogs.

It was a long, narrow room, with a gallery along it for visitors. At the head there was a great iron wheel, about twenty feet in circumference, with rings here and there along its edge. Upon both sides of this wheel there was a narrow space, into which came the hogs at the end of their journey; in the midst of them stood a great burly Negro, bare-armed and bare-chested. He was resting for the moment, for the wheel had stopped while men were cleaning up. In a minute or two, however, it began slowly to revolve, and then the men upon each side of it sprang to work. They had chains, which they fastened about the leg of the nearest hog, and the other end of the chain they hooked into one of the rings upon the wheel. So, as the wheel turned, a hog was suddenly jerked off his feet and borne aloft.

At the same instant the ear was assailed by a most terrifying shriek; the visitors started in alarm, the women turned pale and shrank back. The shriek was followed by another, louder and yet more agonizing—for once started upon that journey, the hog never came back; at the top of the wheel he was shunted off upon a trolley, and went sailing down the room. And meantime another was swung up, and then another, and another, until there was a double line of them, each dangling by a foot and kicking in

frenzy—and squealing. The uproar was appalling, perilous to the eardrums; one feared there was too much sound for the room to hold—that the walls must give way or the ceiling crack. There were high squeals and low squeals, grunts, and wails of agony; there would come a momentary lull, and then a fresh outburst, louder than ever, surging up to a deafening climax. It was too much for some of the visitors—the men would look at each other, laughing nervously, and the women would stand with hands clenched, and the blood rushing to their faces, and the tears starting in their eyes.

Meantime, heedless of all these things, the men upon the floor were going about their work. Neither squeals of hogs nor tears of visitors made any difference to them; one by one they hooked up the hogs, and one by one with a swift stroke they slit their throats. There was a long line of hogs, with squeals and lifeblood ebbing away together; until at last each started again, and vanished with a splash into a huge vat of boiling water. . . .

The carcass hog was scooped out of the vat by machinery, and then it fell to the second floor, passing on the way through a wonderful machine with numerous scrapers, which adjusted themselves to the size and shape of the animal, and sent it out at the other end with nearly all of its bristles removed. It was then again strung up by machinery, and sent upon another trolley ride; this time passing between two lines of men, who sat upon a raised platform, each doing a certain single thing to the carcass as it came to him. One scraped the outside of a leg; another scraped the inside of the same leg. One with a swift stroke cut the throat; another with two swift strokes severed the head, which fell to the floor and vanished through a hole. Another made a slit down the body; a second opened the body wider; a third with a saw cut the breastbone; a fourth loosened the entrails; a fifth pulled them out—and they also slid through a hole in the floor. There were men to scrape each side and men to scrape the back; there were men to clean the carcass inside, to trim it and wash it. Looking down this room, one saw, creeping slowly, a line of dangling hogs a hundred yards in length; and for every yard there was a man, working as if a demon were after him. At the end of the hog's progress every inch of the carcass had been gone over several times; and then it was rolled into the chilling room, where it stayed for twenty-four hours and where a stranger might lose himself in a forest of freezing hogs.

Before the carcass was admitted here, however, it had to pass a government inspector, who sat in the doorway and felt of the glands in the neck for tuberculosis. This government inspector did not have the manner of a man who was worked to death; he was apparently not haunted by a fear that the hog might get by him before he had finished his testing. If you were a sociable person, he was quite willing to enter into a conversation with you, and to explain to you the deadly nature of the ptomaines which are found in tubercular pork; and while he was talking with you you could hardly be so ungrateful as to notice that a dozen carcasses were passing him untouched. This inspector wore a blue uniform, with brass buttons, and he gave an atmosphere of authority to the scene, and, as it were, put the stamp of official approval upon the things which were done in Durham's.

Jurgis went down the line with the rest of the visitors, staring openmouthed, lost in wonder. He had dressed hogs himself in the forest of Lithuania; but he had never expected to live to see one hog dressed by several hundred men. It was like a wonderful poem to him, and he took it all in guilelessly—even to the conspicuous signs demanding immaculate cleanliness of the employees. Jurgis was vexed when the cynical Jokubas translated these signs with sarcastic comments, offering to take them to the secret rooms where the spoiled meats went to be doctored. . . .

With one member trimming beef in a cannery, and another working in a sausage factory, the family had a first-hand knowledge of the great majority of Packingtown swindles. For it was the custom, as they found, whenever meat was so spoiled that it could not be used for anything else, either to can it or else to chop it up into sausage. With what had been told them by Jonas, who had worked in the pickle rooms, they could now study the whole of the spoiled-meat industry on the inside, and read a new and grim meaning into that old Packingtown jest—that they use everything of the pig except the squeal.

Jonas had told them how the meat that was taken out of pickle would often be found sour, and how they would rub it up with soda to take away the smell, and sell it to be eaten on free-lunch counters; also of all the miracles of chemistry which they performed, giving to any sort of meat, fresh or salted, whole or chopped, any color and any flavor and any odor they chose. In the pickling of hams they had an ingenious apparatus, by which they saved time and increased the capacity of the plant—a machine consisting of a hollow needle attached to a pump; by plunging this needle into the meat and working with his foot, a man could fill a ham with pickle in a few seconds. And yet, in spite of this, there would be hams found spoiled, some of them with an odor so bad that a man could hardly bear to be in the room with them. To pump into these the packers had a second and much stronger pickle which destroyed the odor—a process known to the workers as "giving them thirty per cent." Also, after the hams had been smoked, there would be found some that had gone to the bad. Formerly these had been sold as "Number Three Grade," but later on some ingenious person had hit upon a new device, and now they would extract the bone, about which the bad part generally lay, and insert in the hole a white-hot iron. After this invention there was no longer Number One, Two, and Three Grade—there was only Number One Grade. The packers were always originating such schemes—they had what they called "boneless hams," which were all the odds and ends of pork stuffed into casings; and "California hams," which were the shoulders, with big knuckle joints, and nearly all the meat cut out; and fancy "skinned hams," which were made of the oldest hogs, whose skins were so heavy and coarse no one would buy them— that is, until they had been cooked and chopped fine and labeled "head cheese!"

It was only when the whole ham was spoiled that it came into the department of Elzbieta. Cut up by the two-thousand-revolutions-a-minute flyers, and mixed with half a ton of other meat, no odor that ever was in a ham could make any difference. There was never the least attention paid to what was cut up for sausage; there would come all the way back from Europe old sausage that had been rejected, and that was moldy and white—it would be dosed with borax and glycerine, and dumped into the hoppers, and made over again for home consumption. There would be meat that had tumbled out on the floor, in the dirt and sawdust, where the workers had tramped and spit uncounted billions of consumption germs. There would be meat stored in great piles in rooms; and the water from leaky roofs would drip over it, and thousands of rats would race about on it. It was too dark in these storage places to see well, but a man could run his hand over these piles of meat and sweep off handfuls of the dried dung of rats. These rats were nuisances, and the packers would put poisoned bread out for them; they would die, and then rats, bread, and meat would go into the hoppers together. This is no fairy story and no joke; the meat would be shoveled into carts, and the man who did the shoveling would not trouble to lift out a rat even when he saw one—there were things that went into the sausage in comparison with which a poisoned rat was a tidbit. There was no place for the men to wash their hands before they ate their dinner, and so they made a practice of washing them in the water that was to be ladled into the sausage. There were the butt-ends of smoked meat, and the scraps of corned beef, and all the odds and ends of the waste of the plants, that would be dumped into old barrels in the cellar and left there. Under the system of rigid economy which the packers enforced, there were some jobs that it only paid to do once in a long time, and among these was the cleaning out of the waste barrels. Every spring they did it; and in the barrels would be dirt and rust and old nails and stale water—and cartload after cartload of it would be taken up and dumped into the hoppers with fresh meat, and sent out to the public's breakfast. Some of it they would make into "smoked" sausage—but as the smoking took time, and was therefore expensive, they would call upon their chemistry department, and preserve it with borax and color it with gelatin to make it brown. All of their sausage came out of the same bowl, but when they came to wrap it they would stamp some of it "special," and for this they would charge two cents more a pound.

Such were the new surroundings in which Elzbieta was placed, and such was the work she was compelled to do. It was stupefying, brutalizing work; it left her no time to think, no strength for anything. She was part of the machine she tended, and every faculty that was not needed for the machine was doomed to be crushed out of existence. There was only one mercy about the cruel grind—that it gave her the gift of insensibility. Little by little she sank into a torpor—she fell silent. She would meet Jurgis and Ona in the evening, and the three would walk home together, often without saying a word. Ona, too, was falling into a habit of silence—Ona, who had once gone about singing like a bird. She was sick and miserable, and often she would barely have strength enough to drag herself home. And there they would eat what they had to eat, and afterward, because there was only their misery to talk of, they would crawl into bed and fall into a stupor and never stir until it was time to get up again, and dress by candle-light, and go back to the machines. They were so numbed that they did not even suffer much from hunger, now; only the children continued to fret when the food ran short.

Yet the soul of Ona was not dead—the souls of none of them were dead, but only sleeping; and now and then they would waken, and these were cruel times. The gates of memory would roll open—old joys would stretch out their arms to them, old hopes and dreams would call to them, and they would stir beneath the burden that lay upon them, and feel its forever immeasurable weight. They could not even cry out beneath it; but anguish would seize them, more dreadful than the agony of death. It was a thing scarcely to be spoken—a thing never spoken by all the world, that will not know its own defeat.

They were beaten; they had lost the game, they were swept aside. It was not less tragic because it was so sordid, because it had to do with wages and grocery bills and rents. They had dreamed of freedom; of a chance to look about them and learn something; to be decent and clean, to see their child grow up to be strong. And now it was all gone—it would never be! They had played the game and they had lost. Six years more of toil they had to face before they could expect the least respite, the cessation of the payments upon the house; and how cruelly certain it was that they could never stand six years of such a life as they were living!

Discussion Questions

1. How does Jurgis react to the tour of Durham's meatpacking plant?
2. In your own words, describe how working in a meatpacking plant affects Ona and Elzbieta.
3. In your opinion, which details in this excerpt most convincingly highlight problems in the meatpacking industry in the early 1900s?
4. Based on your reading of this excerpt, why do you think Sinclair titled his novel *The Jungle*?

CHAPTER
9
Section 1

AMERICAN LIVES **Robert M. La Follette**
Rebellious Reformer

"[Some people urge] 'standing back of the President,' without inquiring whether the President is right or wrong. For myself, I have never subscribed to that doctrine and never shall."—Robert M. La Follette, Senate speech against a declaration of war (1917)

They called him "Fighting Bob." From his first election to the end of his life, Robert M. La Follette (1855–1925) was a rebel who tried to reform government and end its control by business interests and party bosses.

La Follette, born on a Wisconsin farm, studied at the state university in Madison while working to help support his family. He developed a skill at public speaking and after college joined the Wisconsin bar.

In 1880, he ran for county district attorney against the wishes of the local Republican leader. Visiting every voter he could, he carried the election and won re-election two years later. He then served three terms in the U.S. House of Representatives. The 1890 election was a disaster for Republicans, though, and La Follette lost his seat. Back in Wisconsin, he broke with Philetus Sawyer, the power behind the state Republican party. He charged that Sawyer tried to bribe him to influence a judge in a case that Sawyer was arguing on behalf of a railroad. The exposure of corruption and the break with party leadership launched La Follette's career as a reformer.

He tried several times to win the party's nomination for governor of Wisconsin. Finally, in 1900, La Follette was nominated—and elected. In office he pushed his reform goals: ending party boss control by relying on direct primaries to nominate candidates, making state taxes more fair and equitable by closing business loopholes, and regulating railroad rates. He took his reform plans to the U.S. Senate in 1906.

In the Senate, La Follette again ran afoul of party leaders. He backed the progressive bills that Theodore Roosevelt introduced, but he did not believe the president to be a committed reformer. La Follette hoped to succeed Roosevelt in 1908 as the Republican nominee for president, but the nod, and subsequent election, went to William Howard Taft. As Taft's term proceeded, La Follette grew increasingly critical. In 1911 he sought support for

a presidential run. Once in 1912, tired from overexertion, he delivered a rambling speech that was seen as sign of a nervous breakdown. La Follette's supporters deserted him for Roosevelt and the latter's Bull Moose Party. In the end, Democrat Woodrow Wilson won the election.

La Follette voted for Wilson's progressive measures but resisted U.S. involvement in World War I. He voted against the declaration of war in 1917. He voted against bills creating a military draft and authorizing the use of borrowed money to meet war costs. Senators attacked him for disloyalty, and he was in danger of receiving censure. But the war ended, and Republicans needed his vote to control the Senate. As a result, the censure move died. After the war he opposed the Treaty of Versailles and League of Nations. He felt the treaty would lead only to "an unjust peace which could only lead to future wars."

Conservatives took control of the Republican party in the 1920s, but the independent-minded La Follette continued to rebel. Appalled by corruption in the Harding administration, he led Senate investigations of the Teapot Dome scandal. Uniting the progressives from both parties, he ran for president on a third-party ticket in 1924. Though he spent just a fraction of the money spent by Republicans, he pulled in 5 million votes, one-sixth of the total. He won in Wisconsin and finished second in 11 other states. The next year, Republican Party regulars struck back. They stripped La Follette of his Senate committee assignments, ending his authority. La Follette died soon afterward at age 70.

Questions

1. Cite evidence you find in this biography that supports La Follette's nickname "Fighting Bob."
2. Which of La Follette's reforms do you think had the most lasting impact on American government?
3. How was La Follette punished for rebelling against party leadership?

CHAPTER
9

Section 5

AMERICAN LIVES # Carrie Chapman Catt
Organizer for Women's Rights

"Success [in the struggle for woman suffrage] will depend less on the money we are able to command, than upon our combined ability to lift the campaign above this [internal bickering] . . . and to elevate it to the position of a crusade for human freedom."—Carrie Chapman Catt, speech to woman suffrage leaders (1916)

In 1900, women had struggled to win the right to vote for more than 50 years. That year, Susan B. Anthony retired as leader of the National American Woman Suffrage Association (NAWSA). She chose as her successor Carrie Chapman Catt (1859–1947). By 1920, Catt's "Winning Strategy" had achieved the long-sought goal.

Carrie Lane grew up in the frontier of Iowa, where she learned independence and self-reliance. After graduating from high school, she wanted to attend college but her father refused permission. She worked as a teacher for a year and then entered college as a sophomore, working odd jobs to support herself. After graduation she returned to teaching and quickly became superintendent of schools of a small Iowa city. She married newspaper editor Leo Chapman and worked on his paper. Soon, though, her husband died. In 1890, she attended the first annual meeting of the NAWSA. That same year she married George Catt. A prosperous engineer, he was as committed as his wife to the cause of suffrage. He co-signed a contract with her that stated she would spend one-third of her time in suffrage work.

Catt began to work closely with NAWSA president Susan B. Anthony. She proved to be an exceptional speaker and a skilled organizer and strategist. In 1895 she suggested that NAWSA form an Organizing Committee to coordinate all suffrage efforts. Put in charge of the committee, she trained suffrage workers, organized efforts, and raised money. In 1900, she took over from Anthony as president of NAWSA.

In just a few years, Catt built up NAWSA's organization and treasury. However, her presidency was ended by the illness of her husband. After his death, she devoted herself to pushing for the vote in her home state of New York. By 1915, NAWSA was in trouble. One group wanted to focus on a federal constitutional amendment. This idea was opposed by others who wanted to push the states

first. Needing a strong hand, NAWSA turned to Catt. She agreed to become president, but did not view the task eagerly. "If you have any influence with the divinities," she wrote a friend, "please implore their aid on my behalf."

The next year, Catt launched her "Winning Strategy." In a meeting with NAWSA leaders, she outlined her plan. It combined pushing for a federal constitutional amendment with an active campaign for changes in state constitutions. Catt sensed that gaining partial voting rights for women—voting at least for president, something state legislatures could grant—would in turn create pressure to grant full suffrage through a constitutional amendment.

The next year, the United States entered World War I. Catt urged women to join in the war effort. She believed that such action would help the cause of suffrage. At the same time, she said that NAWSA's "number one war job" was suffrage. The remark drew some criticism. Later that year, New York finally approved women's suffrage. It was an important victory in a populous state and helped convince Congress to approve the Nineteenth Amendment.

In 1919, Catt told NAWSA that it should form the League of Women Voters. She declined to organize it, however, feeling that younger women should take the lead. She devoted the remainder of her life to working for peace groups. She also continued work she had begun in 1902, to encourage woman suffrage in other countries.

Questions

1. What events in Catt's early association with woman suffrage show her dedication to the cause?
2. Why do you think people criticized Catt for saying that NAWSA should remain dedicated to suffrage during World War I?
3. Evaluate Catt as a strategist.

Name _____ Date _____

GUIDED READING *Imperialism and America*

A. As you read this section, fill out the chart below by summarizing reasons why the United States became an imperial power.

The Roots of American Imperialism		
1. Economic roots	2. Political and military roots	3. Racist roots

↓

4. What did Admiral Mahan urge the United States to do to protect its interests?

B. For each year on the time line below, identify one important event in the history of U.S. involvement in Hawaii.

U.S. Imperialism in Hawaii	
1875	
1887	
1890	
1891	
1897	
1898	

C. On the back of this paper, identify who **Queen Liliuokalani** and **Sanford B. Dole** were and explain how their lives were connected.

Name _____ Date _____

A. As you read about the Spanish-American War, write notes in the appropriate boxes
to answer the questions about its causes and effects.

Causes: How did each of the following help to cause the outbreak of the Spanish-American War?
1. American business owners
2. José Martí
3. Valeriano Weyler
4. Yellow journalism
5. De Lôme letter
6. U.S.S. *Maine*

Effects: What happened to each of the following territories as a result of the Spanish-American War?
7. Cuba
8. Puerto Rico
9. Guam
10. Philippine Islands

B. On the back of this paper, explain briefly who **George Dewey** was and what he
did. Then explain the importance of the **Rough Riders** and **San Juan Hill.**

Name _____ Date _____

A. As you read about America's relations with lands under its influence, write notes to answer the questions below. Some answers have already been filled in for you.

	Puerto Rico 1898–1916	Cuba 1898–1903	The Philippines 1898–1945	China 1900
1. What was its relationship to the U.S.?	very similar to that of a colony or protectorate			
2. Why did the U.S. try to control its affairs?			to provide the U.S. with raw materials and new markets	
3. What laws and policies affected its relationship with the U.S.?				
4. What violent events affected its relationship with the U.S.?	Spanish-American War			

B. John Hay's "Open Door notes" paved the way for greater U.S. influence in Asia. Note three beliefs held by Americans that were reflected by the Open Door policy.

1.
2.
3.

C. On the back of this paper, briefly note who **Emilio Aguinaldo** was and how he affected U.S. foreign policy at the turn of the century.

CHAPTER 10

Section 4

GUIDED READING *America as a World Power*

A. As you read this section, write notes summarizing the effects of American military, diplomatic, and economic power around the world.

ROOSEVELT'S "BIG STICK" DIPLOMACY

American action taken	Consequences of that action
1. Treaty of Portsmouth is negotiated.	
2. U.S. warships are used to ensure Panama's independence.	
3. Panama Canal is built.	
4. Roosevelt Corollary is adopted.	

WILSON'S "MISSIONARY" DIPLOMACY

American action taken	Consequences of that action
5. Wilson uses a minor incident with Mexico as an excuse to occupy Veracruz.	
6. Wilson recognizes the Carranza government.	
7. Wilson refuses Carranza's demand to withdraw U.S. troops sent into Mexico to capture Villa.	

B. On the back of this paper, identify **Francisco "Pancho" Villa** and **John J. Pershing**, and describe how their lives came to be interrelated.

America Claims an Empire 27

Name _____   Date _____

A. Completion Select the term or name that best completes the sentence.

William Seward	dollar diplomacy	Roosevelt Corollary
Boxer Rebellion	Alfred T. Mahan	U.S.S. *Maine*
San Juan Hill	Rough Riders	Emilio Aguinaldo

1. The mysterious explosion of the _____ in Havana harbor helped push the United States to declare war against Spain.

2. _____ led the rebellion against American rule in the Philippines.

3. _____ urged that the United States had to strengthen its naval forces before it could become a world power.

4. Critics called the policy of using the U.S. government to promote American business in foreign countries _____.

5. During the Spanish-American War, the _____ were a prominent U.S. regiment of volunteer cavalry.

B. Matching Match the description in the second column with the term or name in the first column. Write the appropriate letter next to the word.

_____ 1. John Hay   a. waterway through Central America

_____ 2. Roosevelt Corollary b. policy of controlling weaker countries

_____ 3. José Martí   c. uprising in China against foreigners

_____ 4. Pearl Harbor   d. agreement ending Spanish-American War

_____ 5. Panama Canal   e. supplement to the Monroe Doctrine

_____ 6. Boxer Rebellion   f. valuable U.S. naval base in Hawaii

_____ 7. Treaty of Paris   g. U.S. official who helped open up China

_____ 8. imperialism   h. Cuban resistance leader against Spain

B. Writing Write a paragraph describing America's actions as an imperial power using the following terms.

Foraker Act   **Platt Amendment**   **protectorate**

CHAPTER 10

Section 2

SKILLBUILDER PRACTICE *Analyzing Bias*

In 1898, senatorial candidate Albert Beveridge gave a campaign speech in which he tried to persuade voters as to why the United States should keep the Philippines. Read this text and then fill in the chart with evidence of bias. (See Skillbuilder Handbook, p. R15.)

God bless the soldiers of 1898, children of the heroes of 1861, descendants of the heroes of 1776! In the halls of history they will stand side by side with those elder sons of glory, and the opposition to the government at Washington shall not deny them. No! They shall not be robbed of the honor due them, nor shall the republic be robbed of what they won for their country. For William McKinley is continuing the policy that Jefferson began, Monroe continued, Seward advanced, Grant promoted, Harrison championed, and the growth of the republic has demanded.

Hawaii is ours; Puerto Rico is to be ours; at the prayer of the people, Cuba will finally be ours; in the islands of the East, even to the gates of Asia, coaling stations are to be ours; at the very least the flag of a liberal government is to float over the Philippines, and I pray God it may be the banner that Taylor unfurled in Texas and Frémont carried to the coast—the stars and stripes of glory.

The march of the flag! . . .

Think of the thousands of Americans who will pour into Hawaii and Puerto Rico when the republic's laws cover those islands with justice and safety! Think of the tens of thousands of Americans who will invade mine and field and forest in the Philippines when a liberal government, protected and controlled by this republic, if not the government of the republic itself, shall establish order and equity there! Think of the hundreds of thousands of Americans who will build a soap-and-water, common-school civilization of energy and industry in Cuba when a government of law replaced the double reign of anarchy and tyranny. Think of the prosperous millions that empress of islands will support when, obedient to the law of political gravitation, her people ask for the highest honor liberty can bestow, the sacred Order of the Stars and Stripes, the citizenship of the Great Republic!

from Thomas B. Reed, ed., *Modern Eloquence,* Vol. XI (Philadelphia, 1903), 224–243.

Words that indicate strong positive feelings	
Words that indicate negative feelings	
Idealized descriptions and images	

CHAPTER 10

Section 1

RETEACHING ACTIIVITY *Imperialism and America*

Finding Main Ideas

The following questions deal with the growth of U.S. imperialism. Answer them in the space provided.

1. What was the policy of imperialism?

_____

_____

2. What three factors fueled the emergence of U.S. imperialism?

_____

_____

3. Why did many business leaders argue that imperialism would help the nation's economy?

_____

_____

4. In what way did Alaska turn out to be a good deal for the United States?

_____

_____

5. How did the country respond to the urgings of Alfred T. Mahan and other proponents of bolstering the country's naval forces?

_____

_____

6. What group became the most powerful in Hawaii? Why did they favor U.S. annexation?

_____

_____

CHAPTER 10
Section 2

RETEACHING ACTIIVITY *The Spanish-American War*

Sequencing

A. Put the events below in the correct chronological order.

_____ 1. Americans learn of de Lôme letter.

_____ 2. The United States declares war on Spain.

_____ 3. U.S. forces arrive in Cuba.

_____ 4. Cubans launch rebellion against Spanish rulers.

_____ 5. Treaty of Paris officially ends the war.

_____ 6. Explosion of the U.S.S. *Maine* stirs war fever in America.

Finding Main Ideas

B. Answer the following questions in the space provided.

1. How did the Treaty of Paris help to make the United States an imperial power?

_____

_____

_____

2. What arguments did opponents of annexing foreign territories present?

_____

_____

_____

CHAPTER 10
Section 3

RETEACHING ACTIIVITY *Acquiring New Lands*

Completion

A. Complete each sentence with the appropriate term or name.

governor	Filipino
protectorate	spheres of influence
Boxers	upper house
Mark Twain	American
lower house	William Jennings Bryan

1. Under the Foraker Act, the United States had the power to appoint Puerto Rico's _____ and _____.

2. The rebellion in the Philippines cost 4,000 _____ lives.

3. The _____ were a group opposed to the growing foreign influence in China.

4. By the late 1800s, China had become home to several European _____, areas where a nation claimed special rights and economic privileges.

5. President McKinley's opponent in the 1900 presidential election was _____, a staunch opponent of imperialism.

Evaluating

B. Write *T* in the blank if the statement is true. If the statement is false, write *F* in the blank and then write the corrected statement on the line below.

_____ 1. The most important reason for the United States to maintain a strong political presence in Cuba was to protect American business interests.

_____

_____ 2. The Supreme Court ruled in the Insular Cases that the U.S. Constitution automatically applied to people in acquired territories.

_____

_____ 3. Many Americans questioned the U.S. presence in Puerto Rico, which was of no strategic importance to the United States.

_____

_____ 4. The United States finally granted the Philippines its independence on July 4, 1946.

_____

_____ 5. Members of the Anti-Imperialist League believed it was wrong for the United States to rule other people without their consent.

_____

Name _____ Date _____

Reading Comprehension

Choose the best answer for each item. Write the letter of your answer in the blank.

_____ 1. Theodore Roosevelt earned the Nobel Peace Prize in 1906 for helping to negotiate a peace treaty to end the war between
   a. England and France.
   b. Russia and Japan.
   c. Cuba and Spain.
   d. China and India.

_____ 2. Before building the Panama Canal, the United States helped to free Panama from its rule by
   a. Colombia.
   b. Nicaragua.
   c. El Salvador.
   d. Mexico.

_____ 3. Construction of the Panama Canal took
   a. 3 years.
   b. 5 years.
   c. 10 years.
   d. 15 years.

_____ 4. The Roosevelt Corollary proclaimed U.S. authority over
   a. Canada.
   b. Asia.
   c. Africa.
   d. Latin America.

_____ 5. The U.S. president most associated with dollar diplomacy was
   a. Theodore Roosevelt.
   b. Woodrow Wilson.
   c. Grover Cleveland.
   d. William Howard Taft.

_____ 6. Woodrow Wislon dispatched General John J. Pershing into Mexico to capture the rebel leader
   a. Porifio Díaz.
   b. Francisco "Pancho" Villa.
   c. Francisco Madero.
   d. Venustiano Carranza.

CHAPTER
10
Section 4

GEOGRAPHY APPLICATION: PLACE
Geography of the Panama Canal

Directions: Read the paragraphs below and study the map carefully.
Then answer the questions that follow.

The Panama Canal is essential to the United States. About 12,000 ships a year pass through the canal, 70 percent of them going to or from U.S. ports.

A ship bound from New York to San Francisco, for example, enters the canal from the Caribbean Sea. The ship remains at sea level for the first few miles. Then it comes to a steplike series of three chambers called locks—the Gatun Locks. Each fills with water after the vessel enters, raising it about 28 feet. The three locks lift the ship to the level of Gatun Lake, formed by Gatun Dam. (It takes 26 million gallons of water from Gatun Lake to fill each lock. The lake does not run dry, however,

because the region receives substantial rainfall and because Gatun Lake has backup water stored in Madden Lake.)

The ship crosses Gatun Lake and goes through the Gaillard Cut, a narrow passage cut through hills. Then the ship is taken into the Pedro Miguel Locks and is lowered about 31 feet to Miraflores Lake. At the other side of the lake, the ship enters the two Miraflores Locks. As the water is released for each, the ship is lowered an additional 27 feet.

At sea level again, the ship passes to the Bay of Panama just a few miles away. The eight-hour passage through the Panama Canal has saved nearly 8,000 miles of travel.

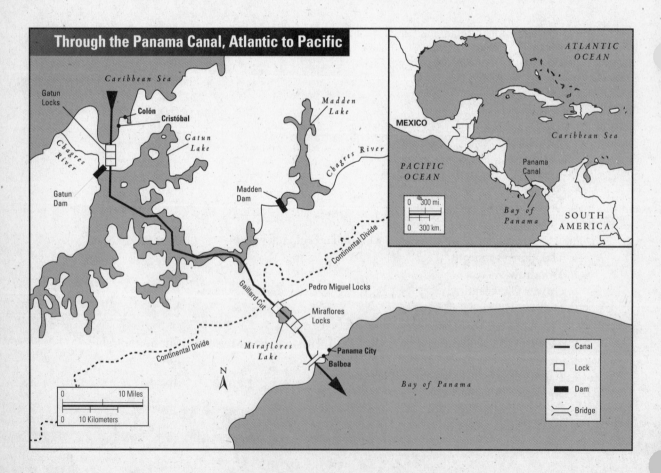

Interpreting Text and Visuals

1. Use a ruler and the map's scale to find the approximate length of the
   Panama Canal. _____

   About how far does a ship travel at sea level when passing through the canal? _____

2. How many locks does the canal have? _____

3. About how many feet above sea level is Gatun Lake? _____

4. Gatun Lake is one of the largest artificial lakes in the world.
   Which river was dammed to create it? _____

5. What topographic obstacle made the Gaillard Cut necessary? _____

   _____

6. It has been noted ironically that although the Atlantic Ocean is east of the
   Pacific Ocean, a ship passing from the Atlantic to the Pacific travels from west to
   east through the Panama Canal. Why is this so?

   _____

   _____

   _____

   _____

   About how many miles east of the Atlantic end of the canal is the Pacific end? _____

7. When the canal was opened in 1914, most of its cargo and passenger traffic was
   bound from one U.S. coast to the other. Today, use of the canal is only the
   eighth most common way of moving U.S. goods and people from coast to coast.
   What are some of the alternatives that have replaced this ocean route?

   _____

   _____

   _____

   _____

Name _____ Date _____

OUTLINE MAP *America As a World Power*

A. Review the maps of U.S. Imperialism, the World, and U.S. Dependencies on textbook pages 356, A2, and A18–19. Then label the following bodies of water and land areas on the accompanying outline map.

Bodies of Water	U.S. Possessions and Protectorates		Other Areas
Pacific Ocean	Cuba	Philippines	Japan
Atlantic Ocean	Guam	Puerto Rico	Australia
Caribbean Sea	Hawaii	Samoa	South America
	Panama Canal Zone	Wake Island	United States
	Midway Island	Alaska	

B. After labeling the map, highlight the areas of U.S. influence outside of its borders and use the completed map to answer the following questions.

1. Which possession or protectorate is farthest from the United States? _____

   About how many miles from the United States is it? _____

2. Which possession or protectorate is located at approximately
   166°E longitude and 19°N latitude? _____

3. Which of the possessions or protectorates was closest to the United States? _____

4. One of the possessions or protectorates served as a refueling station for ships
   traveling from the United States to Australia. Which one do you think it was? _____

5. Give a possible explanation for how Midway Island got its name. _____

   _____

6. Which possessions or protectorates are not islands? _____

7. Describe the path that a ship sailing from Hawaii to the East Coast of the
   United States was likely to take. _____

   _____

8. What is the approximate grid location of Guam? _____

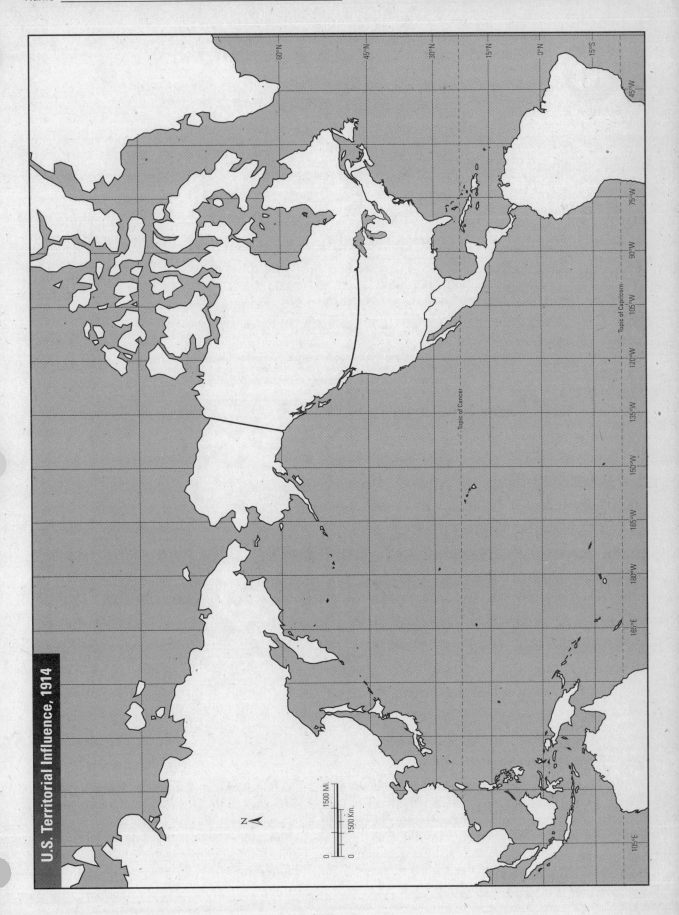

U.S. Territorial Influence, 1914

PRIMARY SOURCE Newspaper Front Page

CHAPTER

10

Section 2

Examine this front page from an edition of Joseph Pulitzer's New York World *printed after the warship U.S.S.* Maine *exploded in Cuban waters. How is this an example of yellow journalism?*

The Granger Collection, New York.

Activity Options

1. Work with a group of classmates to analyze this page from the New York *World*. Are the headlines accurate and reliable? What facts about the sinking of the *Maine* are given? Do you think that the illustration accurately reflects what happened? Draw conclusions about this front page and share them with the class.

2. To understand the difference between yellow journalism in the late 1800s and journalism today, compare this page with the front page of a reputable local or national newspaper. With your classmates, discuss the similarities and differences.

CHAPTER 10

Section 2

PRIMARY SOURCE *from The Rough Riders*
by Theodore Roosevelt

During the Spanish-American-Cuban War, Lieutenant Colonel Theodore Roosevelt led a charge of two African-American regiments and the Rough Riders up San Juan Hill in Cuba. As you read this excerpt from Roosevelt's account of the battle, visualize what happened during the assault.

The infantry got nearer and nearer the crest of the hill. At last we could see the Spaniards running from the rifle-pits as the Americans came on in their final rush. Then I stopped my men for fear they should injure their comrades, and called to them to charge the next line of trenches, on the hills in our front, from which had been undergoing a good deal of punishment. Thinking that the men would all come, I jumped over the wire fence in front of us and started at the double; but, as a matter of fact, the troopers were so excited, what with shooting and being shot, and shouting and cheering, that they did not hear, or did not heed me; and after running about a hundred yards I found I had only five men along with me. Bullets were ripping the grass all around us, and one of the men, Clay Green, was mortally wounded. . . .

I ran back, jumped over the wire fence, and went over the crest of the hill, filled with anger against the troopers, and especially those of my own regiment, for not having accompanied me. They, of course, were quite innocent of wrong-doing; and even while I taunted them bitterly for not having followed me, it was all I could do not to smile at the look of injury and surprise that came over their faces, while they cried out: "We didn't hear you, we didn't see you go, Colonel; lead on now, we'll sure follow you." I wanted the other regiments to come too, so I ran down to where General Sumner was and asked him if I might make the charge; and he told me to go and that he would see that the men followed. By this time everybody had his attention attracted, and when I leaped over the fence again, with Major Jenkins beside me, the men of the various regiments which were already on the hill came with a rush, and we started across the wide valley which lay between us and the Spanish intrenchments.

Captain Dimmick, now in command of the Ninth, was bringing it forward; Captain McBlain

had a number of Rough Riders mixed with his troop, and led them all together; Captain Taylor had been severely wounded. The long-legged men like Greenway, Goodrich, Sharp-shooter Proffit, and others, outstripped the rest of us, as we had a considerable distance to go. Long before we got near them the Spaniards ran, save a few here and there, who either surrendered or were shot down. When we reached the trenches we found them filled with dead bodies in the light blue and white uniform of the Spanish regular army. . . .

There was very great confusion at this time, the different regiments being completely intermingled—white regulars, colored regulars, and Rough Riders. General Sumner had kept a considerable force in reserve on Kettle Hill under Major Jackson of the Third Cavalry. We were still under a heavy fire and I got together a mixed lot of men and pushed on from the trenches and ranch-houses which we had just taken, driving the Spaniards through a line of palm-trees, and over the crest of a chain of hills. When we reached these crests we found ourselves overlooking Santiago.

from Theodore Roosevelt, *The Rough Riders* (New York, 1899). Reprinted in Richard B. Morris and James Woodress, eds., *Voices from America's Past*, Vol. 2, *Backwoods Democracy to World Power* (New York: Dutton, 1963), 276–277.

Discussion Questions

1. Why was Roosevelt angry with the troopers at first?
2. From reading this account, what conclusions can you draw about the Battle of San Juan Hill?
3. After the battle, Roosevelt wrote to his friend Senator Lodge: "I am entitled to the medal of honor, and I want it." Based on your reading of his account, do you agree with Roosevelt? Why or why not?

CHAPTER

10

Section 2

PRIMARY SOURCE In Favor of Imperialism

While running for the Senate in 1898, Indiana's Albert Beveridge gave a campaign speech in which he explained why the United States should keep the Philippines. As you read this excerpt, consider his arguments in favor of U.S. imperialism.

It is a noble land that God has given us; a land that can feed and clothe the world; a land whose coastlines would enclose half the countries of Europe; a land set like a sentinel between the two imperial oceans of the globe, a greater England with a nobler destiny. It is a mighty people that He has planted on this soil; a people sprung from the most masterful blood of history; a people perpetually revitalized by the virile, man-producing working folk of all the earth; a people imperial by virtue of their power, by right of their institutions, by authority of their heaven-directed purposes—the propagandists and not the misers of liberty.

It is a glorious history our God has bestowed upon His chosen people; a history whose keynote was struck by the Liberty Bell; a history heroic with faith in our mission and our future; a history of statesmen who flung the boundaries of the republic out into unexplored lands and savage wildernesses; a history of soldiers who carried the flag across the blazing deserts and through the ranks of hostile mountains, even to the gates of sunset; a history of a multiplying people who overran a continent in half a century; a history of prophets who saw the consequences of evils inherited from the past and of martyrs who died to save us from them; a history divinely logical, in the process of whose tremendous reasoning we find ourselves today.

Therefore, in this campaign, the question is larger than a party question. It is an American question. It is a world question. Shall the American people continue in their restless march toward the commercial supremacy of the world? Shall free institutions broaden their blessed reign as the children of liberty wax in strength, until the empire of our principles is established over the hearts of all mankind? . . .

God bless the soldiers of 1898, children of the heroes of 1861, descendants of the heroes of 1776! In the halls of history they will stand side by side with those elder sons of glory, and the opposition to the government at Washington shall not deny them. No! They shall not be robbed of the honor due them, nor shall the republic be robbed of what they

won for their country. For William McKinley is continuing the policy that Jefferson began, Monroe continued, Seward advanced, Grant promoted, Harrison championed, and the growth of the republic has demanded.

Hawaii is ours; Puerto Rico is to be ours; at the prayer of the people, Cuba will finally be ours; in the islands of the East, even to the gates of Asia, coaling stations are to be ours; at the very least the flag of a liberal government is to float over the Philippines, and I pray God it may be the banner that Taylor unfurled in Texas and Frémont carried to the coast—the stars and stripes of glory.

The march of the flag! . . .

Think of the thousands of Americans who will pour into Hawaii and Puerto Rico when the republic's laws cover those islands with justice and safety! Think of the tens of thousands of Americans who will invade mine and field and forest in the Philippines when a liberal government, protected and controlled by this republic, if not the government of the republic itself, shall establish order and equity there! Think of the hundreds of thousands of Americans who will build a soap-and-water, common-school civilization of energy and industry in Cuba when a government of law replaced the double reign of anarchy and tyranny. Think of the prosperous millions that empress of islands will support when, obedient to the law of political gravitation, her people ask for the highest honor liberty can bestow, the sacred Order of the Stars and Stripes, the citizenship of the Great Republic!

from Thomas B. Reed, ed., *Modern Eloquence*, Vol. XI (Philadelphia, 1903), 224–243.

Discussion Questions

1. Whose hand does Beveridge see in America's destiny?
2. According to Beveridge, what would Hawaii, Puerto Rico, the Philippines, and Cuba gain from their association with the United States?
3. What arguments does Beveridge give for the expansion of the American empire?

CHAPTER 10

Section 4

PRIMARY SOURCE Building the Panama Canal

The Panama Canal took ten years to build and cost almost $400 million. Consider some of the challenges that had to be overcome in building it as you read this excerpt from an eyewitness account of the canal's construction.

From Gatun the train goes through territory which is to be the lake. For twenty-three miles the ships will cross this artificial lake to Culebra Cut. Never before has man dreamed of taking such liberties with nature, of making such sweeping changes in the geographical formation of a country. Here are we Americans dropping down into the heart of a jungle of unequaled denseness, building a young mountain, balancing a lake of 160 odd square miles on the top of the continental divide, gouging out a cañon 10 miles long, 300 feet wide, and in some places over 250 feet deep. Think about that a minute and then be proud that you are an American. . . .

"Look!" my friend cried suddenly. "See that machine—it looks like a steam crane—it is a track-shifter. Invented by one of our engineers. You see, on the dumps, where we throw out the spoil from the cuts, we have to keep shifting the tracks to keep the top of the dump level. Well, it took an awful lot of time to do it by hand. So we developed that machine. It just takes hold of a section of track, rails and ties and all, hoists it up out of its ballast, and swings it over to where we want it. Does in an hour what a gang of twenty men could not do in a week. They're not used much anywhere else in the world. You see, there isn't any other place where they have to shift track on so large a scale."

They seem vastly proud of this track-shifter down here.

"And this is Gorgona," he said, a minute later. "Those shops over there are the largest of their kind in the world—repairing machinery. We can mend anything in there from a locomotive to a watch-spring."

One gets tired of this "largest in the world" talk. But it is only as you accustom yourself to the idea that each integral part of the work is of unequaled proportions that you begin to sense the grandeur of the whole undertaking. The largest dam, the highest locks, the greatest artificial lake, the deepest cut, the biggest machine shops, the heaviest consumption of dynamite, the most wonderful sanitary system—all these and others which I forget are unique—the top point of human achievement. . . .

It is between Gorgona and Empire that you get your first look into Culebra Cut. It is as busy a place as an anthill. It seems to be alive with machinery; there are, of course, men in the cut too, but they are insignificant, lost among the mechanical monsters which are jerking work-trains about the maze of tracks, which are boring holes for the blasting, which are tearing at the spine of the continent—steam shovels which fill a car in five moves, steam shovels as accurate and delicate as a watch, as mighty, well, I can think of nothing sufficiently mighty to compare with these steel beasts which eat a thousand cubic yards a day out of the side of the hills.

But it is not till you get beyond the cut and, looking back, see the profile of the ditch against the sunset that you get the real impression— the memory which is to last. The scars on the side of the cut are red, like the rocks of our great Western deserts. The work has stopped, and the great black shovels are silhouetted against the red of the sky. Then there comes a moment, as your train winds round a curve, when the lowering sun falls directly into the notch of the cut and it is all illumined in an utterly unearthly glory. . . .

from Arthur Bullard, *Panama: The Canal, the Country, and the People* (New York, 1914). Reprinted in Richard B. Morris and James Woodress, eds., *Voices From America's Past*, vol. 2, *Backwoods Democracy to World Power* (New York: Dutton, 1963), 295–298.

Research Options

1. Find out more about the building of the Panama Canal. What obstacles had to be overcome? What dangers did workers face? Prepare a brief oral report and share it with your classmates.
2. Controlling the spread of disease was a key factor in the completion of the Panama Canal. Research how Colonel William C. Gorgas made the Canal Zone safe for workers. Then write a short column about Gorgas's achievement for a health newsletter.

CHAPTER 10

Section 1

LITERATURE SELECTION *from Hawaii*

by James A. Michener

The following excerpt from Michener's sweeping saga deals with the power struggle between native Hawaiians and American sugar planters. As you read this excerpt, think about how the planters seized power from the Hawaiian monarchy. Please be advised that one of the white characters uses an offensive racial epithet.

The revolution that overthrew the Hawaiian monarchy and passed the government into the hands of the sugar planters was under way. In her palace, the wild-willed queen shuddered as she saw American troops file ashore to invade her territory. She was disposed to fight them, for she knew that this was a cruel perversion of the ordinary relationships between sovereign nations, but the sugar planters quickly immobilized her loyal troops, and she was left defenseless, a stubborn, anachronistic woman in her mid-fifties, regal in appearance but totally unaware that the nineteenth century was ebbing to a close and taking with it the concepts of government to which she adhered.

However, in the dying moments of her reign she was not completely without support, for after her troops were disbanded without firing a shot, a squad of volunteer loyalists materialized from the alleys of Honolulu and marched out to defend their queen. In their ranks, and typical of their quality, waddled the old kanaka [a Hawaiian of Polynesian descent] maile [a vine with fragrant leaves and bark] gatherer, Kimo. He had a musket that he had grabbed from a man in a pool hall and he held his uniform—a pair of sagging pants and that was all—about his waist with a length of red rope. His hair had not been combed for some days, he needed a shave and he was barefooted, but like his companions he gave every evidence of being willing to die for his queen. The sparkling American troops with new rifles watched in amazement as the volunteers marched up to give them battle, but a courageous officer in whites ran unarmed to the leader of the irregulars and said, "There's no war. The queen has abdicated."

"She's what?" the leader of the loyalists asked.

"She's abdicated," the young American said. Then he shouted, "Anybody here speak Hawaiian?"

A haole [a person who is not a native Hawaiian] bystander idled up and asked, "What you want, General?"

"Tell these men that there is to be no war. The queen has abdicated."

"Sure," the haole agreed. Turning to Kimo and his men he said, "Eh, you kanaka! Liliuokalani pau. She go home. You pau too. You go home."

And so far as the actual fighting was concerned, in this manner the revolution ended. Kimo trundled his unused musket back to the poolroom and listened to the gibes of his friends. Then in great disturbance of spirit, for he knew that he had participated in the death of a world he had loved—the horses prancing in gold tassels, the royal guard marching in bright uniforms, the queen going forth in a gilt carriage—he walked slowly down Beretania Street and up Nuuanu to the small house where he lived with his wife Apikela and his Chinese family. He went directly to bed and lay there without talking or laughing until he died.

The provisional government, with Micah Hale as its ostensible head and the sugar planters directing from behind, swept away the seventeenth-century anachronisms proposed by Queen Liluokalani. Each act of the efficient new government was directed toward one clear goal: union with America. David Hale and Micah Whipple were rushed to Washington to force a Treaty of Annexation through the Senate before congenial President Harrison and his Republicans left office on March 4, because it was known that the newly elected President, Grover Cleveland, opposed what had been happening in Hawaii; and soon frantic appeals for moral support were speeding back to Honolulu, for the treaty commissioners Hale and Whipple reported: "There is considerable opposition to the manner in which the revolution was carried out. Cannot Micah Hale make a strong statement, relying upon his faultless reputation to give it force? Else we are lost."

It was under these circumstances, in February, 1893, that Micah Hale retired to his study on King Street and wrote for a New York journal: "Any sane man looking at these islands today has got to admit that they require supervision by the United States of America. The indigenous citizens are for the most part illiterate, steeped in idolatry, committed to vain shows of monarchical display and totally unsuited to govern themselves." In these harsh but true words, the son of a missionary, in his seventy-first year, summarized what his group had accomplished; but since he wrote as a profound patriot and as one who loved Hawaii above all else, he did not understand what he was saying. Furthermore, he went on to point out a great truth that others both in Hawaii and America were overlooking: "Hawaii cannot lie idle and unwanted in the middle of the Pacific. The islands seem to lie close to America, but they also lie close to Canada and on the route from that great land to Australia and New Zealand. There is every reason for Hawaii to become Canadian. They also lie close to Russia-in-Asia and except for an accident of history might even now belong to that great power. And to anyone who has sailed from Honolulu to Yokohama or to Shanghai, these islands lie perilously close to Japan and China. For more than half a century I have believed that their destiny lies with America, but it is not as I once thought an inevitable destiny. If at this crucial moment of history, our logical destiny is frustrated, an illogical one will triumph and Hawaii, the gem of the Pacific, will belong to Canada or to Russia or to Japan. It is to prevent such a catastrophe that we pray for the United States to accept us now." This widely reprinted article was taken from the Hale mansion on King Street by Wild Whip Hoxworth and delivered to one of his ships, waiting in the harbor, but as old Micah Hale handed it to his nephew, he was freshly appalled that he should be using such an evil agent to accomplish so good a purpose.

Micah's plea achieved nothing, for Louisiana and Colorado sugar interests prevented the lame-duck Senate of February, 1893, from jamming the Treaty of Annexation through, and five days after Grover Cleveland assumed the Presidency he sternly withdrew the treaty and rebuked those who had sought to foist it upon the American public. Now doleful news reached Hawaii. The Secretary of State wrote: "The United States will not accept the Hawaiian Islands on the terms under which they have been offered. It would lower our national standard to endorse a selfish and dishonorable scheme of a lot of adventurers. I oppose taking these islands by force and fraud, for there is such a thing as international morality."

President Cleveland was of a similar opinion and personally dispatched an investigator to Honolulu to inquire into America's role in the unsavory revolution, and by one of the tricks of history the investigator turned out to be a Democrat from Georgia and a member of a family that had once held slaves. When preliminary news of his appointment reached Hawaii, the Committee of Nine were apprehensive lest he report against them, but when his slave-holding status was revealed, they sighed with visible relief. "As a good Southerner he'll understand our problems," John Janders told the conspirators, and they all agreed.

But Whip Hoxworth, considering the matter carefully, judged: "We may be in for deep trouble. Since Cleveland's investigator comes from Georgia, he probably despises niggers."

"Of course he does," Janders agreed. "He'll see through these Hawaiians right away."

"I doubt it," Whip cautioned. "Granted that he hates niggers. As a sensible human being he'll try to compensate and prove that he doesn't hate other people with dark skins."

"Why would he do that?" Janders demanded.

"Don't ask me why!" Whip replied. "Just watch."

And when the investigator arrived he did exactly as Whip had predicted. Hating Negroes at home, he had to like Hawaiians abroad. It was a profound compulsion and it permitted him, a Georgia man, to understand the revolution better than any other American understood it at the time. He talked principally with Hawaiians, was bedazzled by the idea of speaking directly with a queen, became an ardent royalist, and suppressed evidence given by white men. His report to President Cleveland was a crushing rebuke to the sugar men; they had, he discovered, conspired with the American Minister to overthrow a duly constituted government; they had worked in league with the captain of an American vessel; they had deposed the queen against the will of the Hawaiian people; they had done all this for personal gain; and it was his opinion that Queen Liliuokalani, a virtuous woman, should be restored to her throne.

His report aroused such a storm in Washington that David Hale and Micah Whipple saw there was no hope of forcing the United States to accept Hawaii, and they returned to Honolulu with the glum prediction: "We will never become part of America while Grover Cleveland is President. His Secretary of State is already asking, 'Should not the great wrong done to a feeble state by an abuse of the authority of the United States be undone by restoring the legitimate government?' There's even talk of restoring the queen by force of American arms."

"What would happen to us?" members of the Committee asked.

"Since you're American subjects," a consular official explained, "you'd be arrested, hauled off to Washington, and tried for conspiring to overthrow a friendly power."

"Oh, no!" the conspirators protested. "We're Hawaiian subjects. Our citizenship is here."

September and October, 1893, were uneasy months in Hawaii, and Wild Whip's gang maintained power by only a nervous margin. Each arriving ship brought ominous news from Washington, where sentiment had swung strongly in favor of Queen Liliuokalani, and it was generally assumed that she would shortly be restored to power; but just before this was about to occur the obstinate woman committed an act so appalling to the Americans that she forever discredited the monarchy. What Wild Whip had been unable to gain for himself, the queen won for him.

Late in the year President Cleveland dispatched a second investigator to check upon the specific terms under which Liliuokalani should be returned to her throne, for as Cleveland pointed out, America never wished to profit from the misfortunes of her neighbors. The new investigator plunged the Committee of Nine into despair by announcing that the annexation of Hawaii by America was no longer even under discussion, whereupon he entered into formal discussions with the queen as to what steps she wanted America to take in restoring her crown.

No difficulties were encountered, and the investigator had to smile when the queen pointed out, "One of the charges made against us most often, sir, was that we were a small kingdom overly given to a love of luxurious display. To this charge I must plead guilty, because from the first our kings selected as their advisers men of the missionary group, and we found that no men on earth love panoply and richly caparisoned horses and bright uniforms and medals more than men who have long been dressed in New England homespun. I have four pictures here of state occasions. You see the men loaded with gold and medals. They aren't Hawaiians. They're Americans. They demanded the pomp of royalty, and we pampered them."

"Speaking of the Americans," the investigator asked, "what kind of amnesty will you provide for the revolutionists?"

"Amnesty?" Queen Liliuokalani asked, inclining her large and expressive head toward the American. "I don't understand."

"Amnesty," the investigator explained condescendingly. "It means . . ."

"I know what the word means," Liliuokalani interrupted. "But what does it mean in this circumstance?"

"Hawaii's undergone some unfortunate trouble. It's over. You're restored to your throne. President Cleveland assumes that you'll issue a proclamation of general amnesty. It's usually done."

"Amnesty!" the powerful queen repeated incredulously.

"If not amnesty, what did you have in mind?"

"Beheading, of course," the queen replied.

"What was that?"

"The rebels will have to be beheaded. It's the custom of the islands. He who acts against the throne is beheaded."

The American investigator gasped, then swallowed hard. "Your Excellency," he said, "are you aware that there are over sixty American citizens involved?"

"I did not know the number of traitors, and I do not think of them as Americans. They have always claimed to be Hawaiians, and they shall be beheaded."

"All sixty?" the investigator asked.

"Why not?" Liliuokalani asked.

"I think I had better report to President Cleveland," the perspiring investigator gulped, excusing himself from the august presence; and that night he wrote: "There are factors here which we may not have considered adequately in the past." After that there was no more talk of restoring the monarchy.

Activity Options

1. Acting as the investigator sent to Honolulu by President Cleveland, write up your report on the U.S. role in the revolution. Then share your report with classmates.

2. With a partner, role-play a conversation between a native Hawaiian and a sugar planter on the topic of Hawaii's political problems. Draw on information in this excerpt as well as in your textbook to prepare for your role.

CHAPTER 10

Section 2

AMERICAN LIVES ## José Martí
Poet, Patriot, Inspirational Leader

"It is my duty . . . to prevent, through the independence of Cuba, the U.S.A. from spreading over the West Indies and falling with added weight upon other lands of Our America. All I have done up to now and shall do hereafter is to that end. . . . I know the Monster, because I have lived in its lair."—José Martí, his last letter, written to a friend (1895)

José Martí (1853–1895) spent most of his brief life outside of Cuba, working for Cuba's independence from Spain. A writer and intellectual, he died in combat. A lover of freedom and democracy, he admired U.S. ideals but mistrusted its power and wealth

Martí began his revolutionary activity when he was in his teens. Inflamed by his teacher with the desire for Cuban independence, he began publishing a newspaper called *La Patria Libre* ("Free Homeland") at age 16. He was arrested by Spanish officials and sent to prison. After six months of hard labor in a stone quarry, he was exiled to Spain. Only 18, he was forbidden to return to his country.

Martí studied law in a Spanish university and wrote essays, plays, and poems. His work was full of passion and politics. In 1875, he went to Mexico. Then, after a brief return to Cuba (in disguise, for his safety), he settled in Guatemala, married, and became a teacher and writer. His complete writings eventually filled 73 volumes.

Meanwhile, Cuban rebels were fighting for independence. The Spaniards finally won this ten-year war in 1878. They declared an amnesty, and Martí returned home. However, he continued his anti-Spanish activities, and he was exiled again.

By 1881, Martí had escaped to New York City, where he spent most of the rest of his life. He wrote a novel and more poems. He was hired as a diplomat by Uruguay—and later by Argentina and Paraguay as well. He wrote countless articles for newspapers, explaining Latin America to U.S. readers and explaining the United States to readers throughout Latin America. Most of all, he spent his time promoting the cause of Cuban independence from Spain. Many Cuban tobacco workers lived in Florida. Martí wrote to them and lectured to them, drumming up support for a rebellion. He convinced the workers to donate ten percent of their wages to the cause. He gave lectures to other exiles, setting forth his goals for free Cuba: democracy, widespread education, tolerance between the races, and a varied economy that did not rely on the export of sugar.

He also pushed for Cuba's complete independence from the United States. Economic ties were increasingly linking the island to the United States. Many Cubans hoped that once free from Spanish control, they could join the United States. Martí admired democracy and freedom in the United States, which he called "the greatest [nation] ever built by freedom." However, he believed that capitalism and the growing spirit of imperialism threatened Cuba and all of Latin America. He feared the power of the nation he called "the Monster." His arguments helped convince other Cubans that full independence—not annexation—was the course to follow.

In 1892 Martí organized his supporters into the Cuban Revolutionary Party. He called for another armed rebellion against Spain. He contacted rebels in Cuba and urged them to prepare. He helped organize troops in the United States and elsewhere. In 1895, he announced that the war for independence had begun, and in April he landed in Cuba with a small force of men. On May 19, he was killed by Spanish soldiers in a brief battle. Cuban independence came three years later, and José Martí became a Cuban hero of mythic proportions. A statue of him is found even in New York City.

Questions

1. How did Martí contribute to the movement for Cuban independence?
2. What do Martí's goals for a free Cuba reveal about his thinking?
3. Why did Martí call the United States "the Monster"?

AMERICAN LIVES **William Randolph Hearst**

Successful Publisher, Failed Politician

"[Newspapers are] the greatest force in civilization, . . . [able to] form and express public opinion, . . . suggest and control legislation, . . . declare wars, . . . punish criminals, . . . [and by representing the people] control the nation."
—*William Randolph Hearst, editorial in the New York* Journal *(1898)*

William Randolph Hearst built a great media empire. He published newspapers and magazines, created newsreels, broadcast radio shows, and made movies. However, he never achieved his goal of being a powerful politician.

Hearst (1863–1951) was born to a family made wealthy by owning western mines. He eventually went to Harvard College, where—before being expelled—he became interested in journalism. He persuaded his father to give him a family-owned newspaper, the San Francisco *Examiner*, to run. Hearst hired talented reporters, added new equipment, and printed sensational stories—anything to increase circulation. A letter revealed his view of journalism: "The modern editor of the popular journal does not care for facts. The editor wants novelty. The editor has no objections to facts if they are also novel. But he would prefer novelty that is not fact, to a fact that is not a novelty."

Soon Hearst had won: The *Examiner* had the largest circulation in the city. He determined to compete against Joseph Pulitzer and his New York *World* next. Hearst bought the New York *Journal* and then raided the *World's* staff by offering reporters twice what Pulitzer paid. At the same time, he cut the price of his paper from two cents to one—forcing Pulitzer to cut his price too. He printed sensational stories and promoted his paper constantly. He publicized murders and then sent reporters out to solve them. He used the paper to denounce the Spaniards for their actions in Cuba and to push President William McKinley to declare war. When war finally was declared, Hearst claimed full credit, calling it "the *Journal's* war." The paper's circulation went up.

Hearst added papers in other major cities, including Chicago, Los Angeles, and Boston. He bought magazines. Eventually he added radio stations, a newsreel company, and a film production company. Hearst used these media sources to promote his attempts to enter politics.

He joined the Democratic Party and began to be a power behind the scenes. He used his papers to promote Democratic candidates—and to severely criticize President McKinley. After McKinley was assassinated, Hearst was criticized by many for having aroused hatred of McKinley.

In 1904, Hearst wanted to be the Democratic nominee for president. Largely by using his vast fortune, he secured more than 200 delegates but fell short of the number needed to win. Two years later, he came within 60,000 votes of winning election as governor of New York. He was defeated, in part, by a revival of the charge that his papers' attacks had contributed to the assassination of McKinley. Hearst next tried forming a third party, but the effort failed. He became so unpopular that, when newsreels produced by his company were shown in movie theaters, audiences hissed at his name on the screen.

Hearst returned to the Democrats but was never able to run for public office again. His last political act was to help secure the nomination of Franklin Delano Roosevelt in 1932. Within a few years, though, he had turned against Roosevelt. His papers referred to the president's "New Deal" program as the "Raw Deal." Soon the Depression and Hearst's overspending cut into his fortune. He was forced to sell some of his properties. However, the prosperity of World War II brought back much of his publishing empire by 1945. After a heart seizure in 1947, he spent his remaining years largely as an invalid.

Questions

1. Evaluate Hearst's philosophy of journalism.
2. Hearst served two terms in the House of Representatives, but was not a successful legislator. What in his character would make him unsuitable to be an effective legislator?
3. Assess the timeliness of the opening quotation by Hearst. Is it as accurate in the 21st century as it was in the late 19th century?

Name _____ Date _____

CHAPTER 11
Section 1

GUIDED READING *World War I Begins*

A. As you read this section, take notes to answer questions about the international politics that led to war in Europe.

How did the following help to ignite the war in Europe?				
1. Nationalism	2. Imperialism	3. Militarism	4. Alliances	5. Assassination of Archduke Ferdinand

Why did the following groups of Americans tend to oppose U.S. participation in the war?			
6. Naturalized citizens	7. Socialists	8. Pacifists	9. Parents

What did the following nations do to encourage U.S. participation in the war?		
10. Britain	11. Germany	12. Russia

B. On the back of this paper, identify or define each of the following:

Allies **Central Powers** **"no man's land"** **trench warfare** **Zimmermann note**

CHAPTER 11
Section 2

GUIDED READING *American Power*
Tips the Balance

A. As you read this section, write notes to answer questions about the American experience in World War I.

1. How did the United States raise an army?	2. How did U.S. soldiers help win the war?
3. How did the United States build its naval force?	4. How did the U.S. Navy help win the war?

5. What new weapons of mechanized warfare threatened those in combat?

6. What did the war cost in terms of the number of . . .				7. What were the estimated economic costs?
civilian deaths?	military deaths?	injuries?	refugees?	

B. On the back of this paper, identify or define each of the following:

Alvin York   **conscientious objector**   **Eddie Rickenbacker**

Name _____ Date _____

CHAPTER
11
Section 3

GUIDED READING *The War at Home*

A. As you read this section, take notes to answer questions about how World War I changed American society.

What were some things accomplished by the following wartime agencies and laws?		
1. War Industries Board	2. Railroad Administration	3. Fuel Administration
4. National War Labor Board	5. Food Administration	6. Committee on Public Information
7. Espionage and Sedition Acts		

What changes did the war bring about for the following groups of Americans?		
8. Immigrants	9. African Americans	10. Women

B. On the back of this paper, briefly explain why **Bernard M. Baruch** and **George Creel** are significant historical figures.

CHAPTER
11

Section 4

GUIDED READING *Wilson Fights for Peace*

As you read about President Wilson's plan for world peace, make notes to answer
questions related to the time line below.

1918	Wilson delivers Fourteen Points speech to Congress. →	What were Wilson's points? 1. 2. 3. 4. 5. 6.–13. 14.
1919	Treaty of Versailles is signed. →	15. What terms of the treaty specifically affected Germany?
		16. What were the weaknesses of the treaty?
1920	Senate rejects Treaty of Versailles. →	17. Why did Henry Cabot Lodge object to the treaty?
1921	Senate again rejects Treaty of Versailles. →	18. How did Wilson help bring about the Senate's rejection of the treaty?
	U.S. signs separate treaty with Germany. →	19. What circumstances at this time would eventually lead many Germans to support Adolf Hitler?

Name _____ Date _____

BUILDING VOCABULARY *The First World War*

militarism	Eddie Rickenbacker	George Creel
nationalism	convoy system	Selective Service Act
trench warfare	propaganda	reparations
Archduke Franz Ferdinand	armistice	war-guilt clause

Completion

A. Select the term or name above that best completes the sentence.

1. An intense devotion to the interests and culture of one's nation, known as _____, was one of the long-term causes of World War I.
2. The assassination of _____ in Sarajevo by a Serbian nationalist was the spark that ignited the war.
3. With the help of the _____, which required men to register with the government for possible military service, the United States was able to raise a large fighting force.
4. Through the use of _____, American officials were able to earn much public support for the war.
5. The treaty ending World War I contained a _____, which forced Germany to admit sole responsibility for starting the conflict.

Matching

B. Match the definition in the second column with the word in the first column. Write the appropriate letter next to the word.

_____ 1. militarism   a. laws that imposed penalties for disloyalty

_____ 2. no man's land   b. payment or compensation for war-related damages

_____ 3. Zimmermann note   c. a truce or end to the fighting

_____ 4. convoy system   d. a build-up of armed forces

_____ 5. conscientious objector   e. body that regulated U.S. wartime production

_____ 6. armistice   f. barren region between opposing trenches

_____ 7. Great Migration   g. German letter seeking help from Mexico

_____ 8. War Industries Board   h. one who opposes war on moral grounds

_____ 9. Espionage and Sedition Acts   i. movement of Southern African Americans to the North

_____ 10. reparations   j. use of destroyers to protect merchant ships

Writing

C. Imagine that you are a prominent U.S. political leader in 1919. Use each of the following terms and names correctly in a paragraph either supporting or opposing the peace agreement ending World War I.

Fourteen Points   **League of Nations**   **Treaty of Versailles**   **Henry Cabot Lodge**

CHAPTER
11

Section 1

SKILLBUILDER PRACTICE *Evaluating Alternative Courses of Action*

At the end of 1995, President Clinton was compelled to send U.S. troops to the Balkans. The action brought with it specific questions about the U.S. role in the region. Read the passage about alternatives Clinton faced in 1995. Then evaluate those alternatives by filling in the chart. (See Skillbuilder Handbook, p. 918.)

The Bosnian Conflict During the 1990s, war raged between competing ethnic Serbian and Bosnian factions in the region of Bosnia-Herzegovina. In 1995, the various sides finally negotiated a peace agreement.

One aim of the peace effort was to achieve a more even military balance between the Serbs and the Bosnians and thus ensure that both sides would obey the terms of the peace accord. Throughout the war, Serbian forces had been better trained and better equiped than their Bosnian counterparts. To make the two sides more equal, Bosnian forces needed additional weapons and military training.

Clinton's Alternatives As President Clinton committed 20,000 U.S. soldiers in Bosnia, he had to decide whether to use them only as peacekeepers or to have them arm and train Bosnian troops.

Some of Clinton's advisors favored having U.S. soldiers support the Bosnian forces, claiming that the sooner there was a balance between Serbian and Bosnian power, the sooner American troops could come home. In addition, this course of action would make President Clinton, who was running for reelection, look like a strong leader, unafraid to stand his ground despite political pressure to do otherwise.

Critics of this plan, including U.S. military leaders and European allies, pointed out that arming and training Bosnian forces would put the American troops in additional danger of Serb attack. They remembered other peace efforts when U.S. peacekeeping forces were perceived as siding with one faction over the other. This perception had often resulted tragically in American casualties.

Some advisors suggested that the United States could work through another country, such as Turkey, or through private individuals to arm and train Bosnian forces. With this approach the United States would appear neutral, which would help protect American soldiers. Others pointed out, however, that the world would recognize U.S. participation in the action, and so the risk to American soldiers would remain.

	Alternatives	Pros	Cons	Your evaluation
1.				
2.				
3.				

Name _____ Date _____

CHAPTER 11
Section 1

RETEACHING ACTIVITY *World War I Begins*

Summarizing

Study the information in the chart and refer to it as you complete the sentences that follow.

Causes of The First World War

Rise of Nationalism	Growth of Imperialism	Increased Militarism	Formation of Military Alliances	Igniting Incident
Ethnic groups banded together and became more nationalistic, each demanding their own independent nation.	The race to gain overseas colonies led to heated competition and tension among European countries.	The major powers of Europe had built up great armies and increased their stockpile of weapons.	By 1914, two major alliances had formed in Europe. They would become known as the Allies (France, Great Britain, and Russia) and the Central Powers (Germany, Austria-Hungary, and the Ottoman Empire).	In June of 1914, a Serbian killed Archduke Franz Ferdinand and his wife. Austria-Hungary declared war on Serbia. Russia came to the aid of Serbia. Germany, an ally of Austria-Hungary, declared war in Russia and France. Great Britain then declared war on Germany.

1. Three political situations that led to the beginning of World War I were _____, _____, and _____.

2. The banding together of ethnic groups in a search for greater independence and self-determination resulted from an increasing feeling of _____.

3. _____ was an effort by major European nations to gain more colonies.

4. The two major alliances of Europe would become known as the _____ and the _____.

5. The growth of militarism prompted European nations to increase their _____ and _____.

6. France, Great Britain, and Russia formed the _____.

7. Germany, Austria-Hungary, and the Ottoman Empire became known as the _____.

8. The incident that sparked the beginning of the war was _____.

Name _____ Date _____

RETEACHING ACTIVITY *American Power Tips
the Balance*

Reading Comprehension

A. The statements below are headlines that could have been written during World War I. In the
space provided, write several sentences that support each headline with specific details.

1. America Mobilizes for War

_____

_____

_____

2. New Weapons Change the Fighting

_____

_____

_____

3. The War Takes a Heavy Toll

_____

_____

_____

Evaluating

B. If the statement is true, write *T* in the blank. If the statement is false, write *F* in the blank.
Then write the corrected statement on the line below it.

_____ 1. Under the convoy system, a fleet of destroyers protected merchant ships in the Atlantic Ocean.

_____

_____ 2. The leader of the American Expeditionary Forces was Eddie Rickenbacker.

_____

_____ 3. Alvin York became a hero at the battle of Meuse-Argonne.

_____

_____ 4. Germany agreed to a cease-fire on January 1, 1919.

_____

RETEACHING ACTIVITY *The War at Home*

Outlining

Below is a partial outline of events on the home front during World War I. Complete the outline by adding supporting details for each heading.

I.   Federal Government Takes Greater Control of Economy

A. _____

B. _____

C. _____

II. Washington Attempts to Sell the War

A. _____

B. _____

III. Attacks on Civil Liberties Increase

A. _____

B. _____

IV. The War Encourages Social Change

A. _____

B. _____

Reading Comprehension

Use the following list of words to complete the sentences below.

William Monroe Trotter   George Creel
flu epidemic   Bernard M. Baruch
W. E. B. Du Bois

1. _____ believed that African Americans should support the war effort.

2. The United States and the rest of the world suffered a major_____ during the war years.

3 _____ was the head of the propaganda agency, the Committee on Public Information.

Name _____ Date _____

RETEACHING ACTIVITY *Wilson Fights for Peace*

Reading Comprehension

Choose the best answer for each item. Write the letter of your answer in the blank.

_____ 1. One of President Wilson's Fourteen Points was a call to end
    a. the manufacturing of all weapons.
    b. the use of poison gas.
    c. secret treaties among nations.

_____ 2. A cornerstone of President Wilson's Fourteen Points was the creation of a world peace organization known as the
    a. League of Nations.
    b. United Nations.
    c. World League.

_____ 3. Georges Clemenceau was the premier of
    a. Great Britain.
    b. France.
    c. Italy.

_____ 4. The Treaty of Versailles contained a war-guilt clause, which laid the blame for the conflict on
    a. France.
    b. Germany.
    c. Serbia.

_____ 5. A prominent U.S. leader opposed to the Treaty of Versailles was
    a. Vittorio Orlando.
    b. David Lloyd George.
    c. Henry Cabot Lodge.

_____ 6. During a cross-country speaking tour to win support for the Treaty of Versailles, President Wilson
    a. suffered a paralyzing stroke.
    b. died of a heart attack.
    c. was assassinated.

_____ 7. When the Treaty of Versailles came before the U.S. Senate, the senators
    a. approved it.
    b. rejected it.
    c. approved it with amendments.

_____ 8. World War I came to be known as the
    a. forgotten war.
    b. lost war.
    c. war to end all wars.

GEOGRAPHY APPLICATION: REGION

A New Look for Europe

Directions: Read the paragraphs below and study the maps carefully. Then answer the questions that follow.

In 1919, a peace conference to formally end World War I was held at the Palace of Versailles near Paris. President Wilson, heading the U.S. delegation, had a plan called the Fourteen Points that he hoped would restore stability to Europe.

Of Wilson's points, eight dealt with boundary changes intended to allow European ethnic groups to decide their national identities. Another point called for the formation of a League of Nations to oversee world peace.

However, Wilson's idealism collided with hatred and fear. The French premiere had lived through two German invasions of his country, and he was determined to prevent that from happening again. The British prime minister had just won reelection

with the slogan "Make Germany Pay." Also, contrary to custom, the conference did not include officials of the defeated countries, and Russia and the smaller Allied nations were excluded.

The Treaty of Versailles created nine new nations and changed the boundaries of others. (Shortly thereafter, in 1922–1923, the Soviet Union and Turkey came into being.) But the treaty failed to establish a lasting peace. The U.S. Senate even refused to sign the treaty because of fears that membership in the League would drag the United States into future European squabbles. Many historians blame the flawed treaty for encouraging the conflicts and resentments that surfaced in the 1930s and led to World War II.

Interpreting Text and Visuals

1. What nine new nations were created by the Treaty of Versailles? _____

_____

_____

2. Which countries and empires shown on the prewar map do not appear on the
postwar map?

_____

_____

3. Which prewar countries gained territory from the treaty? _____

_____

4. Out of what nations' lands was Yugoslavia created? _____

_____

5. To what new and already existing countries did Russia lose land? _____

_____

6. Detail what became of the empire of Austria-Hungary after World War I. _____

_____

_____

_____

_____

_____

_____

7. What may have been the reason that Germany was divided into two separate
parts along the Baltic Sea coast after World War I? _____

_____

_____

_____

Name _____ Date _____

CHAPTER
11
Section 1

PRIMARY SOURCE The Zimmermann Note

On January 19, 1917, Arthur Zimmermann, the German foreign minister, sent the following coded telegram to the German ambassador in Mexico. British intelligence agents decoded the telegram and passed it on to the U.S. government. How do you think Americans reacted when this telegram was published on March 1?

Berlin, January 19, 1917

   On the first of February we intend to begin submarine
warfare unrestricted. In spite of this it is our intention
to keep neutral the United States of America.
   If this attempt is not successful we propose an
alliance on the following basis with Mexico: That we shall
make war together and together make peace. We shall give
general financial support, and it is understood that Mexico
is to reconquer the lost territory in New Mexico, Texas,
and Arizona. The details are left for your settlement.
   You are instructed to inform the President of Mexico of
the above in the greatest confidence as soon as it is certain there will be an outbreak of war with the United
States, and we suggest that the President of Mexico on
his own initiative should communicate with Japan suggesting adherence at once to this plan; at the same time
offer to mediate between Germany and Japan.
   Please call to the attention of the President of Mexico
that the employment of ruthless submarine warfare now
promises to compel England to make peace in a few months.
                                              Zimmermann.

from Henry Steele Commager, ed., *Documents of American History*, vol. II, (New York: Crofts, 1947), 308.

Discussion Questions

1. According to this telegram, what did the German government decide to begin on February 1, 1917?
2. What did Zimmermann propose if the United States went to war with Germany during World War I?

3. If this telegram had not been intercepted by British agents, what do you think might have happened? Cite evidence from your textbook to support your opinion.

CHAPTER 11

Section 2

PRIMARY SOURCE Patriotic Song

During World War I, George M. Cohan's rousing "Over There" was a favorite marching song of the American Expeditionary Force. This patriotic song also helped sell thousands of dollars worth of Liberty Bonds when renowned operatic tenor Enrico Caruso sang it on the steps of the New York Public Library. What values and principles do these song lyrics reflect?

Over There

Johnnie get your gun, get your gun, get your gun,
Take it on the run, on the run, on the run;
Hear them calling you and me;
Every son of liberty.
Hurry right away, no delay, go today,
Make your daddy glad, to have had such a lad,
Tell your sweetheart not to pine,
To be proud her boy's in line.

Johnnie get your gun, get your gun, get your gun,
Johnnie show the Hun, you're a son-of-a-gun,
Hoist the flag and let her fly,
Like true heroes do or die.
Pack your little kit, show your grit, do your bit,
Soldiers to the ranks from the towns and the tanks,
Make your mother proud of you,
And to liberty be true.

Chorus
Over there, over there,
Send the word, send the word over there,
That the Yanks are coming, the Yanks are coming,
The drums rum-tumming everywhere.
So prepare, say a prayer,
Send the word, send the word to beware,
We'll be over, we're coming over,
And we won't come back till it's over over there.

from Encyclopaedia Britannica, *1916–1928: World War and Prosperity,* vol. 14 in *The Annals of America* (Chicago: Encyclopaedia Britannica, 1968), 117–118.

Activity Options

1. With two or three classmates, recite the lyrics of "Over There" aloud. Then discuss why you think this song was used as a marching song and why it spurred people to give money for the war effort.

2. Using the sheet music, play or sing the chorus of this song to your classmates.

CHAPTER **11**

Section 3

PRIMARY SOURCE Liberty Bond Poster

Treasury Secretary William G. McAdoo raised millions of dollars for the war effort by selling Liberty Bonds. When people bought these war bonds, they essentially loaned the government money, which was to be paid back with interest at a future date. How did this poster encourage Americans to buy Liberty Bonds?

The Granger Collection, New York.

Research Options

1. Research other methods that the government used to persuade Americans to buy bonds. List these methods and compare your list with those of your classmates.
2. Research the economic impact of Liberty Bonds. How much money was raised for the war through the sale of Liberty Bonds? On average, how much did every American spend on Liberty Bonds? How did the sale of Liberty Bonds affect the national debt? Then discuss your findings with your classmates.

CHAPTER 11

Section 3

PRIMARY SOURCE "Returning Soldiers"
by W. E. B. Du Bois

W. E. B. Du Bois urged African Americans to support the war effort but also criticized racism in the military and on the home front. In May 1919 he published this short essay in The Crisis *magazine. As you read, think about what Du Bois wanted returning African-American soldiers to do.*

We are returning from war! THE CRISIS and tens of thousands of black men were drafted into a great struggle. For bleeding France and what she means and has meant and will mean to us and humanity and against the threat of German race arrogance, we fought gladly and to the last drop of blood; for America and her highest ideals, we fought in far-off hope; for the dominant southern oligarchy entrenched in Washington, we fought in bitter resignation. For the America that represents and gloats in lynching, disfranchisement, caste, brutality and devilish insult—for this, in the hateful upturning and mixing of things, we were forced by vindictive fate to fight, also.

But today we return! We return from the slavery of uniform which the world's madness demanded us to don to the freedom of civil garb. We stand again to look America squarely in the face. . . . We sing: This country of ours, despite all its better souls have done and dreamed, is yet a shameful land.

It *lynches*.

And lynching is a barbarism of a degree of contemptible nastiness unparalleled in human history. Yet for fifty years we have lynched two Negroes a week, and we have kept this up right through the war.

It *disfranchises* its own citizens.

Disfranchisement is the deliberate theft and robbery of the only protection of poor against rich and black against white. The land that disfranchises its citizens and calls itself a democracy lies and knows it lies.

It encourages *ignorance*.

It has never really tried to educate the Negro. A dominant minority does not want Negroes educated. . . .

It *steals* from us.

It organizes industry to cheat us. It cheats us out of our land; it cheats us out of our labor. It confiscates our savings. It reduces our wages. It raises our rent. It steals our profit. It taxes us without representation. It keeps us consistently and universally poor, and then feeds us on charity and derides our poverty.

It *insults* us.

It has organized a nation-wide and latterly a world-wide propaganda of deliberate and continuous insult and defamation of black blood wherever found. It decrees that it shall not be possible in travel nor residence, work nor play, education nor instruction for a black man to exist without tacit or open acknowledgment of his inferiority to the dirtiest white dog. And it looks upon any attempt to question or even discuss this dogma as arrogance, unwarranted assumption and treason.

This is the country to which we Soldiers of Democracy return. This is the fatherland for which we fought! But it is *our* fatherland. It was right for us to fight. The faults of *our* country are *our* faults. Under similar circumstances, we would fight again. But by the God of Heaven, we are cowards . . . if now that that war is over, we do not marshal every ounce of our brain and brawn to fight a sterner, longer, more unbending battle against the forces of hell in our own land.

We *return*.

We *return from fighting.*

We *return fighting.*

Make way for Democracy! We saved it in France, and by the Great Jehovah, we will save it in the United States of America, or know the reason why.

from W. E. B. Du Bois, "Returning Soldiers," *The Crisis* (May 1919), 13–14.

Discussion Questions

1. According to Du Bois, what positive principles did African Americans fight for during World War I?
2. Why does he characterize the United States as "a shameful land"?
3. What fight does he believe should be fought now that African-American soldiers have returned home?
4. Members of Congress accused Du Bois of inciting race riots. What evidence, if any, do you find in this excerpt to support their accusations?

CHAPTER
11

Section 1

LITERATURE SELECTION *from A Son at the Front*
by Edith Wharton

American novelist Edith Wharton lived in France during World War I and wit-nessed the devastation of the war firsthand. As you read this excerpt from her novel, think about the war's impact on John Campton, an American artist living in Paris, and his son, George, a soldier wounded while fighting in the French army.

Campton, from the first, had been opposed to the attempt to bring George to Paris; partly perhaps because he felt that in the quiet provincial hospital near the front he would be able to have his son to himself. At any rate, the journey would have been shorter; though, as against that, Paris offered more possibilities of surgical aid. . . .Well, at any rate, George was alive, he was there under his father's eye, he was going to live; there seemed to be no doubt about it now. Campton could think it all over slowly and even calmly, marvelling at the mira-cle and taking it in. . . So at least he had imagined till he first made the attempt; then the old sense of unre-ality enveloped him again, and he struggled vainly to clutch at some-thing tangible amid the swimming mists. "George—George—George—" he used to say the name over and over below his breath, as he sat and watched at his son's bedside; but it sounded far off and hollow, like the voice of a ghost calling to another.

Who was "George"? What did the name represent? The father left his post in the window and turned back to the bed, once more searching the boy's face for enlightenment. But George's eyes were closed: sleep lay on him like an impenetrable veil. The sleep of ordinary men was not like that: the light of their daily habits continued to shine through the chinks of their closed faces. But with these others, these who had been down into the lower circles of the pit, it was different: sleep instantly and completely sucked them back into the unknown. There were times when Campton, thus watching beside his son, used to say to himself: "If he were dead he could not be farther from me"—so deeply did George seem plunged in secret traffic with things unutterable. . . .

As he sat there, the door was softly opened a few inches and Boylston's face showed through a

crack: light shot from it like the rays around a chal-ice. At a sign from him Campton slipped out into the corridor and Boylston silently pushed a newspa-per into his grasp. He bent over it, trying with daz-zled eyes to read sense into the staring head-lines: but "America—America—America——" was all that he could see.

A nurse came gliding up on light feet: the tears were running down her face. "Yes—I know, I know, I know!" she exulted. Up the tall stairs and through the ramifying of long white passages rose an unwonted rumour of sound, checked, subdued, invisibly rebuked, but ever again breaking out, like the noise of ripples on a windless beach. In every direction nurses and orderlies were speeding from one room to another of the house of pain with the message: "America has declared war on Germany."

Campton and Boylston stole back into George's room. George lifted his eyelids and smiled at them, understanding before they spoke.

"The sixth of April! Remember the date!" Boylston cried over him in a gleeful whisper.

The wounded man, held fast in his splints, con-trived to raise his head a little. His eyes laughed back into Boylston's. "You'll be in uniform within a week!" he said; and Boylston crimsoned.

Campton turned away again to the window. The day had come—had come; and his son had lived to see it. So many of George's comrades had gone down to death without hope; and in a few months more George, leaning from that same window—or perhaps well enough to be watching the spectacle with his father from the terrace of the Tuileries—would look out on the first brown battalions march-ing across the Place de la Concorde, where father and son, in the early days of the war, had seen the young recruits of the Foreign Legion patrolling under improvised flags.

> *"George—George—George—" he used to say the name over and over . . . but it sounded far off and hollow, like the voice of a ghost calling to another.*

At the thought Campton felt a loosening of the tightness about his heart. Something which had been confused and uncertain in his relation to the whole long anguish was abruptly lifted, giving him the same sense of buoyancy that danced in Boylston's glance. At last, random atoms that they were, they seemed all to have been shaken into their places, pressed into the huge mysterious design which was slowly curving a new firmament over a new earth. . .

There was another knock; and a jubilant nurse appeared, hardly visible above a great bunch of lilacs tied with a starred and striped ribbon. . . . George lay smiling, the lilacs close to his pillow, his free hand fingering the envelope; but he did not unseal the letter, and seemed to care less than ever to talk. . . .

When he returned to the hospital after dinner the night-nurse met him. She was not quite as well satisfied with her patient that evening: hadn't he perhaps had too many visitors? Yes, of course—she knew it had been a great day, a day of international rejoicing, above all a blessed day for France. But the doctors, from the beginning, must have warned Mr. Campton that his son ought to be kept quiet—very quiet. The last operation had been a great strain on his heart. Yes, certainly, Mr. Campton might go in; the patient had asked for him. Oh, there was no danger—no need for anxiety; only he must not stay too long; his son must try to sleep.

Campton nodded, and stole in.

George lay motionless in the shaded lamplight: his eyes were open, but they seemed to reflect his father's presence without any change of expression, like mirrors rather than like eyes. The room was doubly silent after the joyful hubbub of the afternoon. The nurse had put the orchids and lilacs where George's eyes could rest on them. But was it on the flowers that his gaze so tranquilly dwelt? Or did he see in their place the faces of their senders? Or was he again in that far country whither no other eyes could follow him?

Campton took his usual seat by the bed. Father and son looked at each other, and the old George glanced out for half a second between the wounded man's lids.

George lay motionless in the shaded lamplight: his eyes were open, but they seemed to reflect his father's presence without any change of expression, like mirrors rather than like eyes.

"There was too much talking today," Campton grumbled.

"Was there? I didn't notice," his son smiled.

No—he hadn't noticed; he didn't notice anything. He was a million miles away again, whirling into his place in the awful pattern of that new firmament. . .

"Tired, old man?" Campton asked under his breath.

"No; just glad," said George contentedly.

His father laid a hand on his and sat silently beside him while the spring night blew in upon them through the open window. The quiet streets grew quieter, the hush in their hearts seemed gradually to steal over the extinguished city. Campton kept saying to himself: "I must be off," and still not moving. The nurse was sure to come back presently—why should he not wait till she dismissed him?

After a while, seeing that George's eyes had closed, Campton rose, and crept across the room to darken the lamp with a newspaper. His movement must have roused his son, for he heard a light struggle behind him and the low cry: "Father!"

Campton turned and reached the bed in a stride. George, ashy-white, had managed to lift himself a little on his free elbow.

"Anything wrong?" the father cried.

"No; everything all right," George said. He dropped back, his lids closing again, and a single twitch ran through the hand that Campton had seized. After that he lay stiller than ever.

George's prediction had come true. At his funeral, three days afterward, Boylston, a new-fledged member of the American Military Mission, was already in uniform.

Activity Options

1. Draw an illustration to accompany this excerpt from the novel. Then show your illustrations to the class and explain your choice of subject matter.
2. What kind of music would you choose to accompany a reading of this excerpt? Play the music for the class and explain why you chose it.

CHAPTER

11

Section 2

LITERATURE SELECTION *from* "In Another Country"
by Ernest Hemingway

The American narrator of Hemingway's short story is seriously wounded near the front lines while serving in the Italian army. He spends a long recuperation in Italy and each day visits a hospital in Milan for physical therapy. As you read this excerpt, think about why the narrator feels the way he does.

There were three boys who came each day who were about the same age as I was. They were all three from Milan, and one of them was to be a lawyer, and one was to be a painter, and one had intended to be a soldier, and after we were finished with the machines, sometimes we walked back together to the Café Cova, which was next door to the Scala [Milan's famous opera house]. . . . Another boy who walked with us sometimes and made us five wore a black silk handkerchief across his face because he had no nose then and his face was to be rebuilt. He had gone out to the front from the military academy and been wounded within an hour after he had gone into the front line for the first time. They rebuilt his face, but he came from a very old family and they could never get the nose exactly right. He went to South America and worked in a bank. But this was a long time ago, and then we did not any of us know how it was going to be afterward. We only knew then that there was always the war, but that we were not going to it any more.

We all had the same medals, except the boy with the black silk bandage across his face, and he had not been at the front long enough to get any medals. The tall boy with a very pale face who was to be a lawyer had been a lieutenant of *Arditi* [a specially trained, elite fighting force] and had three medals of the sort we each had only one of. He had lived a very long time with death and was a little detached. We were all a little detached, and there was nothing that held us together except that we met every afternoon at the hospital. Although, as we walked to the Cova through the tough part of town, walking in the dark, with light and singing coming out of the wine shops, and sometimes having to walk into the street when the men and women would crowd together on the sidewalk so that we would have had to jostle them to get by, we felt held together by there being something that had happened that they, the people who disliked us, did not understand.

We ourselves all understood the Cova, where it was rich and warm and not too brightly lighted, and noisy and smoky at certain hours, and there were always girls at the tables and the illustrated papers on a rack on the wall. The girls at the Cova were very patriotic, and I found that the most patriotic people in Italy were the café girls—and I believe they are still patriotic.

The boys at first were very polite about my medals and asked me what I had done to get them. I showed them the papers, which were written in very beautiful language and full of *fratellanza* [brotherhood] and *abnegazione* [self-sacrifice], but which really said, with the adjectives removed, that I had been given the medals because I was an American. After that their manner changed a little toward me, although I was their friend against outsiders. I was a friend, but I was never really one of them after they had read the citations, because it had been different with them and they had done very different things to get their medals. I had been wounded, it was true; but we all knew that being wounded, after all, was really an accident. I was never ashamed of the ribbons, though, and sometimes, after the cocktail hour, I would imagine myself having done all the things they had done to get their medals; but walking home at night through the empty streets with the cold wind and all the shops closed, trying to keep near the street lights, I knew that I would never have done such things, and I was very much afraid to die, and often lay in bed at night by myself, afraid to die and wondering how I would be when I went back to the front again.

Discussion Questions

1. What three words would you use to describe the narrator's emotional and mental state?
2. In what ways are the narrator and the other soldiers in this excerpt alike and different?
3. How do you explain the detachment that the soldiers in this story feel? Does George Camption in *A Son at the Front* display a similar detachment?

Name _____   Date _____

CHAPTER 11

Section 1

AMERICAN LIVES Jeannette Rankin
Pioneer Advocate of Peace

*"I want to stand for my country, but I cannot vote for war."—Jeannette Rankin,
speech in the House of Representatives (1917)*

Jeannette Rankin was a groundbreaker. In 1917, she became the first woman elected to the House of Representatives. She was also a life-long advocate of peace. She voted in Congress against U.S. entry in World War I and World War II. In 1968, she even led a march protesting the Vietnam War.

Rankin (1880–1973) was raised on a Montana farm. Her parents taught their seven children to make some contribution to society with their lives. After college, Rankin took up teaching and social work. She then joined the fight for woman suffrage. She spoke to the Montana state legislature—the first woman to address that body—arguing that denying women the right to vote amounted to taxation without representation. She helped the National American Woman Suffrage Association (NAWSA) win passage of suffrage laws in North Dakota (1913) and, finally, in her home state (1914). Vowing to "repay the women of Montana who had worked for suffrage," she ran for one of Montana's two seats in the House. She campaigned for a national suffrage law, laws to protect children, prohibition, and staying out of World War I. She defeated seven other candidates to win the Republican primary and then won the general election despite a Democratic landslide.

Reaching Washington in April 1917, she was immediately given a difficult decision. President Woodrow Wilson asked Congress to declare war on Germany. Rankin received pressure from woman suffrage advocates on both sides. Carrie Chapman Catt feared that a vote against the war would make women look disloyal. Alice Paul urged a no vote, declaring that women should stand for peace, not war. Rankin voted no. Though 49 other House members joined her, criticism of her was intense. The New York *Times* said the vote "justified distrust of her judgment."

During her term, Rankin worked to achieve the goals she had campaigned for. She introduced the nation's first bill aimed at improving health care for women and newborns, a bill that became law in

1921. She helped lead the floor fight for a suffrage amendment, although it did not pass. Hoping to keep a statewide office in the 1918 election, she ran for one of Montana's Senate seats but lost.

Out of office, Rankin became increasingly committed to the cause of peace and worked for various causes over the next two decades. Mistrusting the foreign policy of President Franklin Roosevelt and fearing U.S. involvement in World War II, she ran again for Congress in 1940. Her position was popular in Montana and she won the election. However, public opinion shifted after the Japanese attacked Pearl Harbor. The next day, when Congress voted in favor of Roosevelt's declaration of war against Japan, Rankin again voted no. This time, though, hers was the only such vote. She was widely criticized. Newspaper editor William Allen White commended her for her courage, but noted that she "stood firm in folly." Any hope that she had of re-election was dashed, and she declined to run for office again.

Rankin opposed aggressive steps taken during the Cold War, the postwar ill will between the United States and the Soviet Union. She traveled to encourage the peace movement around the world. As the Vietnam War raged in the 1960s, she entered the public eye again. In 1968 the 88-year-old Rankin led a march of 5,000 women to protest that war. She began to consider running again for Congress to carry out the peace campaign, but poor health prevented her.

Questions

1. Rankin said denying women the vote was taxation without representation. Was this a valid claim? Why or why not?
2. Which vote—1917 or 1941—do you think was more difficult for Rankin? Explain why.
3. Review Rankin's stands against U.S. involvement in war over the decades. Do they seem responsible or irresponsible? Defend your choice either way.

CHAPTER **11**

Section 3

AMERICAN LIVES *Oliver Wendell Holmes, Jr.*
Thinker in Action

*"War, when you are at it, is horrible and dull. It is only when time has passed
that you see that its message was divine. . . . But some teacher of the kind we
all need. In this smug, over-safe corner of the world we need it, that we may
realize that our comfortable routine is no eternal necessity of things."*
—Oliver Wendell Holmes, Jr., Memorial Day speech (1895)

He joined the Union army while he was still in college and fought with distinction in the Civil War. At age 61, he took a seat on the Supreme Court, where he served for 30 years. Oliver Wendell Holmes, Jr., (1841–1935) dedicated most of his 94 years to serving his country. His goal throughout was to put his mind and learning to work on important questions.

Two influences shaped Holmes's life. First was his background. He came from a line of prominent New England families. His father was an admired doctor and famous author. Holmes developed a deep love for New England traditions. At the same time, he was not bound by these traditions. He questioned what he read. He had a probing mind.

Second was the Civil War. The war broke out as he was completing college. He enlisted and after graduation marched to the front as a second lieutenant. In his three years in the army, Holmes was wounded three times—once so severely that he was given up for dead. The war gave him a sense of a larger purpose in life and shaped his career. Holmes's questioning mind had led him to philosophy. However, a desire for public service aroused by his war duty led him to the law. He wanted not just to think but "to think for action."

After graduating from law school in 1866, Holmes combined a legal practice with intense study. He also worked as editor of the *American Law Review* and he taught. In 1881 he revealed his legal philosophy in *The Common Law.* "The life of the law has not been logic," he wrote. "It has been experience." To know the law, a person had to understand its present interpretation and the past that shaped it.

The next year, Holmes was named to the Massachusetts Supreme Court. After twenty years on that bench, he joined the U.S. Supreme Court, where he remained for 30 years. When he resigned in 1932, the 90-year-old Holmes said it was time to "bow to the inevitable."

He judged cases in light of his idea of the law. "The provisions of the Constitution," he wrote, "are not mathematical formulas. . . . They are organic living institutions." However, he was careful not to impose his own opinions on a case. A judge may disagree with a law, he believed, without the law becoming unconstitutional.

Holmes wrote hundreds of decisions, some for the majority and some in dissent, explaining his reasons for disagreeing with the majority decisions. Two of his most famous opinions, both from 1919, involve free speech. First was *Schenck* v. *United States.* Charles Schenck had been convicted of trying to interfere with the military draft during World War I. Schenck argued that the arrest violated his right to free speech. Holmes wrote the opinion of the unanimous majority that upheld the convictions. The government has the right to restrict speech, he wrote, when the speech presents a "clear and present danger" to society. The context in which speech occurs determines whether the speech is protected. The first amendment does not protect someone from "falsely shouting fire in a theater and causing a panic."

That same year, Holmes wrote a minority opinion in *Abrams* v. *United States* that urged allowing free speech in another context. Abrams had been convicted of distributing pamphlets that criticized the government's war policy. The majority upheld the convictions. Holmes argued that the pamphlets represented free speech.

Questions

1. What value did Holmes see in war?
2. What does Holmes mean by saying that law is based on experience, not solely on logic?
3. Why did Holmes rule differently in the two free speech cases, *Schenck* and *Abrams*?

Answer Key

Chapter 9, Section 1
GUIDED READING

A. Possible answers:

Social Reforms

1. People: the YMCA; the Salvation Army; settlement houses; Florence Kelley

   Successes: a variety of public services; the Illinois Factory Act

2. People: the WCTU; Frances Willard; the Anti-Saloon League

   Successes: prohibition adopted by many town and state governments

3. People: Eugene V. Debs; American Socialist Party; muckrakers; Ida M. Tarbell

   Successes: exposure of corruption in industry

4. People: Frederick Winslow Taylor; Ford Motor Co.; Henry Ford

   Successes: Ford Assembly line; the "Five Dollar Day"

5. People: National Child Labor Committee; Louis Brandeis; Florence Kelley; Josephine Goldmark

   Successes: Keating–Owen Act; state child-labor laws; *Muller* v. *Oregon; Bunting* v. *Oregon;* workers' compensation laws

Political Reforms

6. People: Hazen Pingree; Tom Johnson

   Successes: commission and council-manager forms of government adopted; the property tax, public ownership of utilities, and other economic reforms

7. People: Robert M. La Follette, Charles B. Aycock, James Hogg

   Successes: Wisconsin laws regulating railroads

8. People: William S. U'Ren

   Successes: states adopted the secret ballot, initiative, referendum, recall, and direct primary; Seventeenth Amendment

B. Answers will vary widely depending upon the specifics noted.

Chapter 9, Section 2
GUIDED READING

A. Possible answers:

1. Lower Class: agricultural; domestic; manufacturing

   Middle and Upper Class: white-collar jobs

   African American: agricultural; domestic

   Immigrant: agricultural; domestic; piecework; taking in boarders; manufacturing

2. New women's colleges established

3. Marriage was no longer a woman's only alternative; offered opportunities to pursue a profession; offered opportunities to devote oneself to volunteer work and reform movements

4. a. Tried to convince state legislatures to grant women the right to vote

   b. Pursued court cases to test the Fourteenth Amendment

   c. Campaigned for a national constitutional amendment to grant women the vote

5. a. Wyoming, Utah, Colorado, and Idaho granted women the vote; efforts in other states failed.

   b. The Supreme Court ruled that women were citizens, but that citizenship did not automatically confer the right to vote.

   c. It was always voted down.

B. Answers will vary widely depending upon the specifics noted.

Chapter 9, Section 3
GUIDED READING

A. Possible answers:

1. Roosevelt: Called both sides to the White House to negotiate; threatened to take over the mines

   Legislation: None

2. Roosevelt: Filed suits under the Sherman Antitrust Act against many trusts

   Legislation: Sherman Antitrust Act

3. Roosevelt: Urged Congress to strengthen the Interstate Commerce Act; fought for passage of the Elkins Act and Hepburn Act

   Legislation: Interstate Commerce Act; Elkins Act; Hepburn Act

4. Roosevelt: Appointed a commission to study the meatpacking industry; pushed for passage of the Meat Inspection Act

   Legislation: Meat Inspection Act; Pure Food and Drug Act

5. Roosevelt: Promoted conservation of natural resources; set aside thousands of acres of forest reserves, water-power sites, wildlife sanctuaries, and national parks; named a professional conservationist to head the U.S. Forest Service; promoted large-scale irrigation projects

   Legislation: National Reclamation Act (Newlands Act)

6. Roosevelt: None or Appointed an African American as head of the Charleston, South Carolina, customhouse; refused to dismiss an African-American postmistress in Mississippi; invited Booker T. Washington to dinner

   Legislation: None

B. Answers will vary widely depending upon the specifics noted.

Chapter 9, Section 4
GUIDED READING

A. Possible answers:

1. Progressives: Opposed Taft because he had signed and defended the Payne-Aldrich Tariff, seemed to oppose conservation, and supported conservative boss Joseph Cannon

   Conservatives: Supported Taft because they opposed progressivism, Roosevelt, and low tariffs and because they favored business

2. Progressives: Progressive or Bull Moose Party

   Conservatives: Republican party

3. Progressive: Theodore Roosevelt

   Republican: William Howard Taft

   Democratic: Woodrow Wilson

   Socialist: Eugene V. Debs

4. Progressive: Supported government action to supervise big business, but did not oppose all big business monopolies

   Republican: Favored business, but

worked to break up trusts

Democratic: Supported small business and free market competition

Socialist: Felt that big business was evil and that the solution involved doing away with capitalism and distributing wealth

B. Answers will vary widely depending upon the specifics noted.

Chapter 9, Section 5
GUIDED READING

Possible answers:

1. Federal Trade Act: Set up the Federal Trade Commission with power to investigate corporations and unfair business practices

2. Clayton Antitrust Act: Strengthened the Sherman Antitrust Act; freed labor unions and farm organizations from antitrust laws; prohibited most injunctions against strikers

3. Underwood Tariff: Substantially reduced tariff rates for the first time since the Civil War

4. Sixteenth Amendment: Legalized a federal income tax

5. Federal Reserve Act: Established the Federal Reserve System, a decentralized private banking system under federal control

6. Increased activism of local and grass roots groups; the use of new strategies to build enthusiasm; regeneration of the national movement under Carrie Chapman Catt

7. The Nineteenth Amendment

8. Opposed federal antilynching legislation; appointed segregationists to his cabinet; failed to oppose the resegregation of federal offices

Chapter 9
BUILDING VOCABULARY

A.

1. c	2. h
3. e	4. b
5. j	6. i
7. g	8. f
9. d	10. a

B.

1. T

2. F—The major goal of the prominent progressive governor Robert M. La Follette was reforming the nation's railroad industry.

3. F—The goal of the NAACP was equal rights among the races.

4. T

5. T

C. Answers will vary depending on the specifics noted.

Chapter 9, Section 1
SKILLBUILDER PRACTICE

Who: Who were the boys in these mines? Who were the companies that employed them? Who was responsible for enforcing the child-labor laws?

What: What is the Children's Bureau? What is the Philadelphia Compensation Law?

When: When did these practices begin? When—if ever—were they stopped?

Where: Where is this coal-mining region?

Why: Why was the report undertaken? Why was "public opinion" uneffective?

How: How were the workers endangered? How could their safety have been ensured?

Chapter 9, Section 1
RETEACHING ACTIVITY

Goal—protecting social welfare
Example—Social Gospel and settlement house movements sought to help the poor; YMCA offered activities to city-dwellers; the Salvation Army fed the poor and cared for children; Illinois Factory Act prohibited child labor and limited women's working hours;
Goal—promoting moral improvement
Example—Women's Christian Temperance Union led crusade for prohibition;
Goal—creating economic reform
Example—American Socialist Party forms in opposition to capitalist system; muckrakers expose corruption in business and public life;

Goal—fostering efficiency
Example—reformers apply scientific management techniques to the workplace in order to make workers more productive and efficient

Chapter 9, Section 2
RETEACHING ACTIVITY

1. twenty percent; garment workers, jobs in offices, stores, and classrooms

2. as domestic workers on farms or as cooks, laundresses and maids in the nation's large cities

3. These amendments extended the right to vote to African American men, but not to women.

4. Workplace reform, housing reform, educational improvement, and food and drug laws

5. Liquor industry—feared that women would vote in support of prohibition; textile industry—worried that women would vote for restrictions on child labor; many men—concerned about the changing role of women in society

6. Attempt to convince state legislatures to grant women the right to vote; try to achieve voting rights through the court system; push for a constitutional amendment to grant women the vote

Chapter 9, Section 3
RETEACHING ACTIVITY

1. b	2. a
3. d	4. c
5. a	6. b

Chapter 9, Section 4
RETEACHING ACTIVITY

A.

1. T

2. F—The presidential election of 1912 saw the emergence of new third party, the Progressive Party, also known as the Bull Moose Party.

3. F—Woodrow Wilson, the 1912 Democratic presidential candidate, was a reform governor from New Jersey.

4. T

5. The Bull Moose Party finished second behind the Democratic Party in the election of 1912.

B.

1. He signed the compromise Payne-Aldrich Tariff, which only moderated the high tariffs of the Aldrich Bill.

2. He appointed as secretary of the interior Richard A. Ballinger, who opposed conservationist measures in western lands and removed 1 million acres of forest and mining lands from the protected list.

3. He fired the prominent conservationist Gifford Pinchot from the U.S. Forest Service.

Chapter 9, Section 5
RETEACHING ACTIVITY

1. Princeton University

2. New Freedom

3. monopolies

4. farm organizations, labor unions

5. Underwood Act

6. Idaho

7. Nineteenth Amendment

8. segregationists

9. opposed

10. World War I

Chapter 9, Section 5
GEOGRAPHY APPLICATION

Responses may vary on the inferential questions.

1. Wyoming; 30 years

2. Colorado, Utah, and Idaho

3. the West; the Southeast, mid-Atlantic, and New England regions

4. Illinois became the first state where the new strategy of women gaining partial voting rights through legislative action became successful.

5. The U.S. Constitution allows states the right to determine simply through legislative action who is eligible to vote for presidential electors. Therefore, voting for president in this indirect manner could be given to women without states putting the question to a popular vote, as is done for constitutional amendments.

6. full suffrage

7. In 1913 Illinois granted women the right to vote for president. This opened up the conservative Midwest to granting women this partial voting right. The change in attitude helped make New York's full-suffrage vote possible. The victory in populous New York then gave the movement sufficient strength in Congress to pass the Nineteenth Amendment in 1919—which was ratified by the states in 1920.

Chapter 9, Section 1
PRIMARY SOURCE

Declaration of the WCTU

1. Students may say the WCTU believed in everlasting life, the Golden Rule, one standard of purity for men and women, equal rights of all to hold opinions and express them, a living wage, an 8-hour day, courts of conciliation and arbitration, justice, and "peace on earth and goodwill to men."

2. They pledged to abstain from alcohol and to discourage the consumption and sale of alcohol. They also pledged to work and to pray that their principles would become part of society and its laws.

3. Goal: promoting moral improvement

Chapter 9, Section 1
PRIMARY SOURCE

Child Labor in the Coal Mines

1. Informally assess students' diary entries. Entries should reflect the nature of the work the boy engages in as well as his thoughts and feelings about the coal mines.

2. Informally assess students' letters for clarity, coherency, and persuasiveness. Before students begin, you may want to provide them with models of letters to the editor.

Chapter 9, Section 2
PRIMARY SOURCE

Political Poster

1. Through their research, students may find that woman suffragists used some of the following: posters, lobbying, pamphlets, parades and rallies, newspaper and magazine articles. Informally assess students' discussion about which methods could be used effectively today.

2. Through their research, students may find out that Josephine Dodge, a wealthy widow, founded the organization, which was based in her Fifth Avenue apartment in New York City. Dodge and her followers were concerned that women's spiritual and moral role would be diminished if they did gain the vote. Informally assess students' posters to make sure they reflect the spirit of the National Association Opposed to Woman Suffrage.

Chapter 9, Section 2
PRIMARY SOURCE

"The Status of Woman"

1. Students are likely to mention that Anthony feels that women have come closer to gaining the vote, citing the growth of the National American Woman Suffrage Association, successful efforts on state and national levels, the enfranchisement of women in Wyoming, and efforts to pass a Sixteenth Amendment.

2. Some students will say that her attitude is optimistic and positive because she believes it will happen eventually. Other students may say that her attitude is one of frustration, since she points out that much time and energy has been consumed.

Chapter 9, Section 3
LITERATURE SELECTION

The Jungle

1. Jurgis is awed by the plant's efficient, clean, productive atmosphere and is innocently taken in by all that he sees on the tour.

2. Students may say that they are numb, exhausted, and desensitized to the death and the unsavory practices all around them.

3. Responses will vary but should include specific details from the selection that points to problems in the meatpacking industry.

4. Some students might say that the title reflects the brutality of the meatpacking industry.

Chapter 9, Section 1
AMERICAN LIVES

Robert M. La Follette

Possible responses:

1. La Follette once broke with his state party leader over a bribery attempt. He repeatedly tried to become his party's nominee for governor. He failed to consider Roosevelt as a true reformer, and this angered party leaders. He dared to resist U.S. involvement in World War I. He led Senate investigations into the Teapot Dome scandal.

2. La Follette's most lasting reform was the primary election for nominating candidates, which opened public office to those not backed by party leaders.

3. La Follette was punished by party leaders for his rebelliousness by withholding nominations from him. Also, near the end of his life he had his Senate committee seats taken away from him.

Chapter 9, Section 5
AMERICAN LIVES

Carrie Chapman Catt

Possible responses:

1. She spent at least a third of her time promoting suffrage. She worked closely with NAWSA president Susan B. Anthony while she trained others and raised money.

2. To some people, Catt's idea that NAWSA had a goal other than dedicating itself to the war effort might seem disloyal.

3. Catt was a very good strategist: her notion that state support was necessary to win ratification of a federal constitutional amendment proved to be effective.

Chapter 10, Section 1
GUIDED READING

A. Possible answers:

1. Industrial overproduction in the U.S. led to the view that the country's factories needed raw materials from abroad and that surplus U.S. products needed to be sold in new markets.

2. The global military expansion of European powers led to a U.S. desire to do the same.

3. Belief in the racial and cultural superiority of Anglo-Saxons led many to claim that the U.S. had a responsibility to expand and spread Christianity and civilization.

4. Build up its naval power

B. Possible answers:

1875: A treaty allows Hawaiian sugar to be sold in the U.S., duty-free.

1887: American business leaders force the king to change Hawaii's constitution, so that only wealthy landowners have voting rights; the U.S. forces Hawaii to allow an American naval base at Pearl Harbor.

1890: The McKinley Tariff eliminates the duty-free status of Hawaiian sugar.

1891: Liliuokalani becomes Queen of Hawaii.

1897: William McKinley, who favors annexation, becomes U.S. president.

1898: Congress proclaims Hawaii an American territory.

C. Answers will vary widely depending upon the specifics noted.

Chapter 10, Section 2
GUIDED READING

A. Possible answers:

1. Business: Urged U.S. intervention to protect American business interests in Cuba

2. Martí: Provoked U.S. intervention by deliberately destroying American-owned sugar mills and plantations

3. Weyler: Took harsh actions against the Cuban people, including forcibly removing them to camps, where thousands died

4. Yellow journalism: Encouraged the American public to sympathize with Cuban rebels and the war

5. De Lôme letter: Angered the American public because of its criticism of President McKinley

6. *Maine:* Led to widespread support for war; led McKinley to ask Congress to declare war

7. Cuba: Achieved independence from Spain

8. Puerto Rico: Went from Spanish to American rule

9. Guam: Went from Spanish to American rule

10. Philippine Islands: Sold by Spain to the U.S.; annexed by the U.S.

B. Answers will vary widely depending upon the specifics noted.

Chapter 10, Section 3
GUIDED READING

A. Possible answers:

1. Puerto Rico: [Provided]

   Cuba: Protectorate; very similar to that of a colony

   Philippines: Very similar to that of a protectorate or colony

   China: "Trading partner"

2. Puerto Rico: Its location was of strategic importance to the U.S.

   Cuba: To protect American business

   Philippines: [Provided]

   China: To establish and protect new markets in China

3. Puerto Rico: Treaty of Paris; Foraker Act; imperialist policies

   Cuba: Platt Amendment; imperialist policies

   Philippines: Treaty of Paris; removal policy; imperialist policies

   China: Open Door policy; imperialist policies

4. Puerto Rico: [Provided]

   Cuba: Spanish-American War

   Philippines: Spanish-American War; Philippine-American War

   China: Boxer Rebellion

B. Possible answers:

1. The U.S. economy relied on exports to ensure growth.

2. The U.S. had the right to intervene abroad to keep foreign markets open to it.

3. U.S. survival was threatened by the closing of an area to American products, citizens, or ideas.

C. Answers will vary widely depending upon the specifics noted.

Chapter 10, Section 4
GUIDED READING

A. Possible answers:

1. The Russo-Japanese War ended; the Nobel Peace Prize awarded to Roosevelt; American prestige increased

2. Rights to build a canal, to control the canal zone, and to intervene in Panama gained by the U.S.; the Panama Canal built; U.S.-Latin American relations severely damaged

3. Travel time between Atlantic and Pacific reduced; the power and prestige of the U.S. enhanced; U.S.-Latin American relations severely damaged

4. U.S. adoption of dollar diplomacy; U.S. military interventions in Latin America, specifically Nicaragua

5. Deaths of at least 200 Mexicans; U.S. and Mexico brought close to war

6. U.S. comes into conflict with Pancho Villa.

7. Anti-American feeling in Mexico intensified; Mexico nationalizes oil and mineral resources, adopts strict regulations on foreign investors

B. Answers will vary widely depending upon the specifics noted.

Chapter 10
BUILDING VOCABULARY

A.

1. U.S.S. *Maine*

2. Emilio Aguinaldo

3. Alfred T. Mahan

4. dollar diplomacy

5. Rough Riders

B.

1. g	2. e	3. h
4. f	5. a	6. c
7. d	8. b	

C. Answers will vary depending on the specifics noted.

Chapter 10, Section 4
SKILLBUILDER PRACTICE

strong positive: heroes; glory; growth; the flag of a liberal government; the stars and stripes of glory; justice and safety; order and equity; energy and industry; prosperous millions

negative: opposition to the government at Washington; robbed of the honor; double reign of anarchy and tyranny

idealized: the highest honor liberty can bestow; the Sacred Order of the Stars and Stripes; the citizenship of the Great Republic

Chapter 10, Section 1
RETEACHING ACTIVITY

1. the policy in which stronger nations would extend their economic, political, or military control over weaker territories

2. desire for military strength; thirst for new markets; belief in cultural superiority

3. It would provide raw materials for the nation's factories and new markets for its agricultural and manufactured goods.

4. For about two cents an acre, the nation acquired a land rich in timber, minerals, and oil.

5. The U.S. built nine steel-hulled cruisers and became the world's third largest naval power.

6. American sugar planters; annexation would allow them to deliver sugar to the United States without having to pay any duties.

Chapter 10, Section 2
RETEACHING ACTIVITY

A.

1. 2	2. 4
3. 5	4. 1
5. 6	6. 3

B.

1. It gave the U.S. the islands of Guam and the Philippines in the Pacific, and Puerto Rico in the Caribbean.

2. Some felt that it violated the Declaration of Independence by denying self-government to newly-acquired territories. African-American leaders argued that the U.S. should settle race issues at home before taking on social problems elsewhere. Labor leaders feared that new immigrants would compete for American jobs.

Chapter 10, Section 3
RETEACHING ACTIVITY

A.

1. governor; upper house

2. American

3. Boxers

4. Spheres of influence

5. William Jennings Bryan

B.

1. T

2. F—The Supreme Court ruled in the Insular Cases that the U.S. Constitution did not automatically apply to people in acquired territories.

3. F—Many Americans questioned the U.S. presence in Puerto Rico, which nevertheless was strategically important to the United States, both for maintaining a U.S. presence in the Caribbean and for protecting a future canal through Panama.

4. T

5. T

Chapter 10, Section 4
RETEACHING ACTIVITY

1. b	2. a
3. c	4. d
5. d	6. b

Chapter 10, Section 4
GEOGRAPHY APPLICATION

Responses may vary on the inferential questions.

1. about 50 miles (or 80 kilometers); about 10 miles (or 16 kilometers)

2. six

3. about 85 feet

4. the Chagres River

5. the hills forming the Continental Divide

6. The narrow strip of land through which the canal passes contains a northwest bend. Therefore, its Atlantic end is actually northwest of its Pacific end; about 27 miles.

7. Today many faster means of transport—such as cars, trucks, trains, planes, and even pipelines—are used to move goods and people from coast to coast.

Chapter 10, Section 4
OUTLINE MAP

1. the Philippines; about 8,500 miles

2. Wake Island

3. Cuba

4. Samoa

5. Possible answers: It is about in the middle of the Pacific Ocean; it is located almost exactly on 180° longitude, which is halfway, or midway, around the world from 0° longitude.

6. Panama Canal Zone and Alaska

7. A ship would sail southeast about 5,000 miles, cross through the Panama Canal Zone, and then head northeast around Cuba to the United States.

8. about 144°E longitude and 13°N latitude

Chapter 10, Section 2
PRIMARY SOURCE

Newspaper Front Page

1. Informally assess students' analyses and conclusions. Students will likely find that the headlines and illustration on this page sensationalize the possible causes and effects of the explosion.

2. You may wish to provide students with local and national newspapers before they begin this activity. Informally assess students' discus-

sion comparing the two front pages.

Chapter 10, Section 2
PRIMARY SOURCE

The Rough Riders

1. He was angry because they ignored his command to follow him and charge the next line of trenches.

2. Students might conclude that fighting was fierce, that the charge uphill was physically demanding, that many Spanish soldiers died in the battle, that Roosevelt and his men acted bravely, and that the capture of Santiago was an important victory.

3. Some students might agree because Roosevelt showed courage in leading the charges up San Juan Hill. Others might point out that Roosevelt risked the lives of his men when he failed to communicate clearly with the troopers.

Chapter 10, Section 2
PRIMARY SOURCE

In Favor of Imperialism

1. God's hand

2. Hawaii and Puerto Rico would gain justice and safety, the Philippines would gain order and equity, and Cuba would gain a government of law and an end to tyranny and anarchy.

3. Students might mention his economic and commercial arguments, including the rich resources that the United States would gain as a result of expansion. They may also mention that the United States in the past has successfully expanded beyond its boundaries.

Chapter 10, Section 4
PRIMARY SOURCE

Building the Panama Canal

1. Informally assess students' oral reports. Through their research, they may find that workers faced mud slides, rock slides, premature dynamite explosions, and diseases such as malaria and yellow fever.

2. Students' columns may include information related to how Gorgas direct-

ed a drainage project that eradicated the disease-bearing mosquito. To eliminate the mosquitos' breeding places, he drained as much standing water as he could and covered any remaining standing water with oil. He also cut grass, burned garbage, paved streets, and covered windows with fine screens. As an alternative, you may want to have students create a version of the *Canal Record* by researching and reporting on the canal construction project.

Chapter 10, Section 1
LITERATURE SELECTION

Hawaii

1. Informally assess students' reports. As an alternative, you may want to have students act as journalists reporting on the Hawaiian crisis.

2. Informally assess the conversations held between students. Remind them to stay in character as they discuss Hawaii's political problems.

Chapter 10, Section 2
AMERICAN LIVES

José Martí

Possible responses:

1. Martí organized political and economic support for a renewed fight for independence.

2. Martí's goals show him to be a democrat concerned with justice—shown by his desire for racial tolerance—and economic development—shown by his favoring widespread education and a diversified economy.

3. Martí called the United States "the Monster" because he feared its economic power and growing imperialist ideology.

Chapter 10, Section 2
AMERICAN LIVES

William Randolph Hearst

Possible responses:

1. Hearst's sensational journalism, with little regard for facts, is dangerous because democracy depends on the truthful exchange of information.

2. Hearst probably failed as a legislator because he was accustomed to making decisions and seeing them carried out—not to having to work with others toward a common goal.

3. Hearst's notion of the power of the press seems accurate today. Newspapers still break scandals, reveal corruption, and sway public opinion.

Chapter 11, Section 1
GUIDED READING

A. Possible answers:

1. Nationalism: Encouraged competitiveness and antagonism among nations; made various ethnic groups want to establish independent nations of their own

2. Imperialism: Encouraged competitiveness and antagonism between nations

3. Militarism: Led to military build-ups and a naval arms race

4. Alliances: Committed nations to support one another if attacked

5. Assassination: Led Austria-Hungary to declare war against Serbia, which automatically brought in nations involved in the alliance system

6. Naturalized citizens: Had close ties to their home nations

7. Socialists: Saw the war as an imperialist struggle

8. Pacifists: Believed that all wars are evil

9. Parents: Didn't want their sons to experience the horrors of warfare and to die

10. Britain: Cut the transatlantic cable between Germany and the U.S.; emphasized accounts of German aggression in its news reports to the U.S.; gave the U.S. large orders for war materials and took out large loans from the U.S.

11. Germany: Engaged in unrestricted submarine warfare; sank the *Lusitania* and other ships carrying Americans; promised to give Mexico American territory

12. Russia: Overthrew the czar and established a representative government, creating a situation in which the war became one of democracy *versus* dictatorships

B. Answers will vary widely depending upon the specifics noted.

Chapter 11, Section 2
GUIDED READING

A. Possible answers:

1. Called for volunteers; instituted a draft (Selective Service Act)

2. Brought freshness and enthusiasm; helped stop German advances on Paris and several other French cities; helped win the Second Battle of the Marne; mounted offenses at St. Mihiel and Meuse-Argonne

3. Called for volunteers; instituted a draft (Selective Service Act); accepted women volunteers; exempted shipyard workers from the draft; ran a public relations campaign to emphasize the importance of shipyard work; began using prefabrication to construct ships; took over commercial and private ships and converted them for war use

4. Broke the German blockade by suggesting the convoy system to the British and then putting it into practice; helped lay down a barrier of mines across the North Sea

5. Zeppelins (gas-filled airships); machine guns; tubes that spewed poison gas; tanks; airplanes

6. Civilian deaths: more than 11 million

   Military deaths: around 11 million

   Injuries: 20 million

   Refugees: 10 million

7. Economic costs: about $338 billion

B. Answers will vary widely depending upon the specifics noted.

Chapter 11, Section 3
GUIDED READING

A. Possible answers:

1. War Industries Board: Encouraged companies to use mass production techniques and to standardize products; set production quotas; allocated raw materials; conducted psychological testing to help people find the right jobs; increased industrial production by about 20 percent; caused retail prices and corporate profits to soar

2. Railroad Administration: Controlled the nation's railroads

3. Fuel Administration: Regulated coal supplies; rationed gasoline and heating oil; introduced daylight-savings

4. National War Labor Board: Resolved labor disputes; pushed for improved working conditions

5. Food Administration: Encouraged Americans to reduce their consumption of food voluntarily; tripled food shipments to the Allies; set a high government price for wheat and other staples

6. Committee on Public Information: Mobilized the nation's artists and advertising people to popularize the war; recruited 75,000 Four Minute Men to deliver pro-war speeches; increased support for the war

7. Espionage and Sedition Acts: The prosecution of 2,000 people and the convictions of more than 1,000; loss of mailing privileges for publications that criticized the war; firing of people opposed to the war; imprisonment of Eugene V. Debs, Emma Goldman, and Bill Haywood

8. Immigrants: Many lost their jobs; some were attacked or killed.

9. African Americans: The Great Migration involved the massive movement of African Americans from Southern rural areas to Northern cities. It caused new problems for African Americans as they began to live in cities, but it also improved their economic opportunities. African-American soldiers were allowed for the first time to serve under African-American officers.

10. Women: Many women moved into jobs traditionally held by men. Women's wartime efforts encouraged passage of the Nineteenth Amendment, which recognized their right to vote.

B. Answers will vary widely depending upon the specifics noted.

Chapter 11, Section 4
GUIDED READING

Possible answers:
1. open treaties
2. freedom of the seas
3. tariffs lowered or abolished to encourage free trade
4. arms reduction
5. consideration of the interests of

colonial peoples

6.–13. boundary changes and self-determination of ethnic/national groups

14. a League of Nations

15. Demilitarization; return of Alsace-Lorraine to France; $33 billion in reparations; war-guilt clause

16. Humiliated Germany; set Germans against the treaty; set reparations that Germany couldn't possibly pay; ignored the sacrifices and desires of Russia; stripped Germany of the colonies it needed to pay reparations; ignored the claims of colonized peoples for self-determination

17. Suspicious of the provision for joint action against aggression; wanted the treaty to declare the constitutional right of Congress to declare war

18. Chose an American delegation that failed to include enough Republicans and Senators; refused to compromise with Lodge

19. political instability and violence; resentment over Germany's treatment by the Allies

Chapter 11
BUILDING VOCABULARY

A.
1. nationalism
2. Archduke Franz Ferdinand
3. Selective Service Act
4. propaganda
5. war-guilt clause

B.
1. d   2. f   3. g   4. j
5. h   6. c   7. i   8. e
9. a   10. b

C. Answers will vary.

Chapter 11, Section 1
SKILLBUILDER PRACTICE

Sample response:

Alternative 1: Americans serve only as peacekeepers.

Pros: Less risk to American soldiers

Cons: May take longer to achieve balance between Serbs and Bosnians. Serbs might overrun Bosnians again.

Evaluation: Not such a good idea

Alternative 2: Have American troops arm and train Bosnians.

Pros: Gets Americans out of Bosnia soon; makes president look strong

Cons: Risks Serb attack on Americans.

Evaluation: A good choice; the risk would be small.

Alternative 3: Have another country arm and train Bosnians.

Pros: U.S. would look neutral.

Cons: Serbs would see that U.S. was behind it anyway; risk to Americans.

Evaluation: Not such a great idea; a cowardly way to handle problem

Chapter 11, Section 1
RETEACHING

1. any three of the following: nationalism, imperialism, militarism, military alliances, the assassination of Archduke Franz Ferdinand
2. nationalism
3. Imperialism
4. weapons, armed forces
5. Allies, Central Powers
6. Allies
7. Central Powers
8. the assassination of Archduke Franz Ferdinand and the quick retaliation by Austria-Hungary

Chapter 11, Section 2
RETEACHING

A.
1. Congress has passed the Selective Service Act, which requires men to register for military service. Some 24 million men have registered, and almost 3 million were have been called up for duty. Meanwhile, the government has aided the building of warships.
2. World War I has introduced new weapons, including tanks and poison gas and has ushered in the use of planes for military purposes. Also, the machine gun has become more refined. These powerful weapons have made warfare more deadly.
3. The war has claimed around 22 million lives, more than half of them civilians. In addition, some 20 million people have been wounded, and 10 million have become refugees. The total financial cost has been about

$340 billion.

B.
1. T
2. The leader of the American Expeditionary Forces was General John J. Pershing.
3. T
4. Germany agreed to a cease-fire on November 11, 1918.

Chapter 11, Section 3
RETEACHING

A.

I.
A. Government establishes War Industry Board to supervise war production.
B. Wilson establishes National Labor Board to settle disputes between management and labor.
C. Wilson sets up Food Administrat to produce and conserve

II.
A. Government raises taxes and selling o
B. Government estab on Public Informat public support for

III.
A. Immigrants from G Austria-Hungary suf tion and violence.
B. Congress passes Espi Sedition Acts, which and jail sentences for with the war effort.

IV.
A. Numerous war-related thousands of African A move from the South t North in the Great Mig
B. Women take advantage related job opportunitie into the working world.

B.
1. W. E. B. Du Bois
2. flu epidemic
3. George Creel

Chapter 11, Section 4
RETEACHING

1. c   2. a   3. b   4. b
5. c   6. a   7. b   8. c

Chapter 11, Section 4
GEOGRAPHY APPLICATION

Responses may vary on the inferential questions. Sample responses are given.

1. Austria, Hungary, Yugoslavia, Czechoslovakia, Poland, Latvia, Lithuania, Estonia, and Finland
2. Austria-Hungary, the Ottoman Empire, Montenegro, Serbia, and Russia
3. France, Italy, Romania, and Greece
4. Austria-Hungary, Montenegro, and Serbia
5. Finland, Estonia, Latvia, Lithuania, Poland, and Romania

...parate nations of Austria... were established... middle of... food. ...rest of... money through... war bonds. ...ishes Committee ...ion to stir up ...he war effort.

...rmany and ...er discrimina- ...onage and ...pose fines ...interfering

...jobs prompt ...mericans to ...cities in the ...ration. ...of new war- ...to move.

Chapter 11
PRIMARY SOURCE

Patriotic Song

1. Informally assess groups' analyses. Remind them to consider the music as well as the lyrics.
2. Encourage all students to sing the chorus.

Chapter 11, Section 3
PRIMARY SOURCE

Liberty Bond Poster

1. Students might mention any of the following: rallies; parades; speeches by the Four-Minute Men; bond drives; newspaper and billboard ads; sales talks between theater acts; promotion by such movie stars as Douglas Fairbanks, Mary Pickford, and Charlie Chaplin.
2. Students may find that bonds raised about $21 million for the war effort, that every American spent an average of $400 on bonds, and that heavy borrowing caused the national debt to soar from $1 billion in 1914 to $27 billion in 1919.

Chapter 11, Section 3
PRIMARY SOURCE

...rning Soldiers"

...le responses:

...r the liberation of France, for ...reedom, for America's ideals

...because the United States does not treat all of its citizens fairly and subjects African Americans to lynching, disenfranchisement, discrimination in education, cheating, and insults

3. the fight for democracy, equality, and justice in the United States
4. Some students may say that Du Bois uses inflammatory language and urges his readers to fight for democracy. Others may say that this excerpt contains no evidence that Du Bois incited race riots.

Chapter 11, Section 1
LITERATURE SELECTION

A Son at the Front

1. Informally assess students' illustrations for appropriateness of content and sensitivity.
2. Informally assess students' choice of music on the basis of sensitivity to the selection and individual effort.

Chapter 11, Section 2
LITERATURE SELECTION

"In Another Country"

Possible responses:

1. detached, lonely, afraid
2. Similarities: the narrator and the other soldiers are all wounded officers, have the same medals, and feel detached from the people around them. Differences: the narrator received his medal because he is an American fighting for a European cause; the others are Italian. Also, the men suffered different injuries.
3. The detachment may be a result of the brutal, dehumanizing experience of war. The soldiers are not free of the war, since they will be sent back, and so they exist in a sort of limbo between life and death. George in *A Son at the Front* also appears detached and only rallies briefly when he hears news of America's entry into the war.

Chapter 11, Section 1
AMERICAN LIVES

Jeannette Rankin

Possible responses:

1. Rankin's claim was valid: women were taxed but had no opportunity to vote.
2. The 1941 vote—coming after the attack on Pearl Harbor was probably harder for Rankin.
3. Some students may find it difficult to justify Rankin's stands.

Chapter 11, Section 3
AMERICAN LIVES

Oliver Wendell Holmes, Jr.

Possible responses:

1. To Holmes, war can shake people out of being too comfortable. He also valued the service that war demands.
2. Law, to Holmes, is not a rigid set of rules. It is a changing set of rules affected by society.
3. In *Schenck*, people had tried to interfere with the draft. This was a "clear and present danger" to the government. In *Abrams*, the people were simply speaking out against the war.